Ho
Pe

2018

with
World Peace Directory

65th Edition   ISSN 0957-0136

Published and distributed by

HOUSMANS BOOKSHOP
5 Caledonian Road, Kings Cross, London N1 9DX, UK
(tel +44-20-7837 4473; email diary@housmans.com)

ISBN 978 0 85283 279 0

Editorial co-ordination — Albert Beale
Cover design & month illustrations — Kate Evans
Dates & quotations compilation — Bill Hetherington
Historical research — Bill Hetherington
Lay-out & production — Chris Booth, graphics.coop

Directory from Housmans Peace Resource Project,
editor Albert Beale (www.housmans.info)

Copyright © 2017 Housmans Bookshop Ltd

Printed by Russell Press Ltd, Nottingham, on FSC paper

Personal Notes

Name

Address

Telephone

_____

_____

_____

_____

_____

_____

_____

_____

_____

_____

_____

_____

_____

EXPLANATORY NOTES

National public holidays in the UK, Republic of Ireland, Canada and the USA are noted by the abbreviation HOL, followed by abbreviations for relevant countries: ENG – England, NI – Northern Ireland, SCOT – Scotland, W – Wales; UK – United Kingdom (ie all the preceding four); IRE – Republic of Ireland; CAN – Canada; US – United States. We regret that we are not able to show holidays in other countries.

Dates of moon phases, solstices and equinoxes are for UTC; users in other time zones will find that the local date is different in some cases.

ORDERING INFORMATION

Copies of the Diary may be ordered from:
Housmans, 5 Caledonian Road, Kings Cross, London N1 9DX, UK (tel +44-20-7837 4473; email orders@housmans.com)

Introduction

Welcome to the 65th edition of the Housmans Peace Diary, intended as both a resource and an inspiration for campaigners around the world.

This year's feature, as with several recent editions, takes up a First World War centenary theme. We compare state and intergovernmental activities at the end of the war with actions by conscientious objectors and war resisters; and we look at the burgeoning of new movements in that period – including the Women's International League for Peace and Freedom, the International Fellowship of Reconciliation, the No More War Movement, War Resisters' International, and – later – International Voluntary Service for Peace and the Peace Pledge Union.

The feature looks at efforts by anti-militarists to ensure that commemorations of war are inclusive of all who suffer, that they recognise that civilians now far outnumber the military among the dead and maimed, and that they also emphasise the urgent need for renunciation of war.

The main Diary pages include a fresh selection of weekly quotations and daily anniversaries.

Noteworthy anniversaries include the bicentenary of the death of Quaker pioneer William Penn, and the centenary of the gaoling of antimilitarist socialist Eugene Debs for opposing US participation in WW1. We also mark the 90th anniversary of the Treaty of Paris, when major states purported to repudiate war (but didn't), the 80th of the death of nonviolent theorist Bart de Ligt, the 75th of the beheading of Hans & Sophie Scholl for White Rose leafletting in Nazi Germany, the 70th of the assassination of Gandhi, the 60th of the first Aldermaston March against nuclear weapons, the 50th of the assassination of Martin Luther King, the 40th of the challenge to bishops by the Anglican Pacifist Fellowship to debate war, the 30th of *glasnost* & *perestroika*, leading to the end of the Cold War, and the 20th of the death of pacifist composer Michael Tippett.

The Diary and its World Peace Directory are a non-profit service to fellow activists, depending on much voluntary labour. We welcome promotional help – leaflets are available from Housmans Diary Group, 5 Caledonian Road, Kings Cross, London N1 9DX; email diary@housmans.com. We are grateful for all who have helped in many ways over the past year.

HOUSMANS DIARY GROUP

The need to end war, not just wars

The First World War is seen as the earliest example of mass warfare on a cataclysmic scale. But it didn't only usher in a new style of warfare, it also encouraged the foundation of new sorts of peace campaigns – ones built on both a more total and a more personal rejection of warfare than had been common in earlier years. Much of the pacifist and anti-militarist parts of today's peace movements have origins in the responses to the nationalism and militarism of a century ago.

And the lessons that should have been learned from the outbreak of the First World War are reflected in the lessons, also unlearned, from the *ending* of that war: lessons such as the need to prioritise reconciliation over retribution, and the need to remember past wars with symbols of regret and a commitment to change, not in a spirit of patriotism and bombast.

In the following pages, in the centenary year of the nominal ending of WW1, we look at aspects of the evolution of our struggles against war, during the period from "the war to end all wars" to the world we find ourselves in – and the world we are still trying to remake – today.

A war ends

"At eleven o'clock this morning came to an end the cruellest and most terrible war that has ever scourged mankind. I hope we may see that thus, this fateful morning, came an end to all wars." So David Lloyd George, British Prime Minister, addressed the House of Commons on 11 November 1918.

He did not mention that the Armistice had actually been agreed at five o'clock, but the announcement was delayed for the dramatic solemnity of the eleventh hour of the eleventh day of the eleventh month; never mind stray fatal shots during those final six hours of what eventually came to be widely acknowledged as a pointless conflict.

Such cynicism was echoed a few days later in Lloyd George's General Election promise "to make Britain a fit country for heroes to live in". It was not long before the worst slump in British history, the "heroes" standing on street corners begging, not for money, but for jobs. If it was bad in Britain, it was worse for erstwhile enemies; there was rampant inflation in Germany, so that within a few years of the war a one mark note was overprinted a hundred, a thousand, even a million marks, but was actually worth more as fuel for heating than for purchases. Many, especially children, were starving in Austria. If physical proof were ever wanted that war creates more problems than it purports to solve, these events provided it.

Nevertheless, after a Conference beginning on 18 January 1919, the Peace Treaty was signed at Versailles on 28 June, officially ending war between Germany and the Allies (five years to the day since Archduke Franz Ferdinand's assassination, the putative *casus belli*); there were parallel treaties with Austria and Turkey. The treaties supposedly established a new era of European tranquillity; from the collapsed Russian, German and Austrian empires, the old Baltic states, plus Finland and Poland, re-emerged, together with Czechoslovakia as a unified state. Yet, as we now know, within twenty years all were to be involved in a new war, and – excepting Finland – were embroiled in the ensuing 45 years of Cold War. So much for the vaunted "end to all wars". Indeed, as early as 1918–20 Lloyd George ordered an abortive expedition to northern Russia in support of White Russian opposition to the Bolshevik government.

Over the years, the peace treaty itself came to be criticised by peace movements as unbalanced. It was drafted by the Allies, before German representatives were called in to accept or refuse it – refusal inevitably meaning resumption of the war. It included an article enunciating German "war guilt", and requiring financial reparations to be paid, regardless of Germany's devastated economy. It was generally accepted in later years that "war guilt" and reparations contributed to the rise of the populist, and totalitarian, Adolf Hitler.

A more positive element of the Treaty had been fore-seen by the poet Alfred Tennyson, among others, as far back as 1842 – "the war-drum throbbed no longer and the battle flags were furled In the Parliament of man, the Federation of the world". Though not actually a federation, the League of Nations was established on 10 January 1920, with headquarters in traditionally neutral Switzerland, but its effectiveness was dimin-ished by the isolationist US Senate's refusal to endorse US membership, despite President Woodrow Wilson's enthusiasm. Ultimately, after the failure to deal with Japanese creation of a puppet state in Manchuria in 1931–2, the abortive Disarmament Conference of 1932–4, Italy's takeover of Abyssinia in 1935, and effectively being sidestepped by the four-power (UK, France, Germany, Italy) purported "settlement" of the 1938 crisis over Czechoslovakia, the League faded way before formal dissolution on 18 April 1946. Its replacement, the United Nations, has lasted consider-ably longer, even if not necessarily more successfully – although UN agencies, some inherited from the League, are mostly regarded as having a more creditable record.

Movements emerge...

One element of the post-WW1 British peace movement was the League of Nations Union (LNU), an active support group for the League; but close co-operation with it by pacifist groups was difficult, since the LNU was committed to the principle of Collective Security, as it was called – the term was a euphemism for a commitment to go to war in support of any League member state under attack.

The so-called Peace Ballot of British households (organised by the LNU over 1934–5) was often decried as a vote for pacifism, whereas – as it was designed to do – it actually endorsed Collective Security. A notable person who for a long time did not appreciate the distinction was Vera Brittain. After her experience as a

Voluntary Aid Detachment nurse in France during WW1, and the death in the war of her brother (her only sibling), her fiancé, and two close friends, she committed herself from 1921 to work for peace as an LNU speaker. Then, in June 1936, she was invited to share a platform in Dorchester with Dick Sheppard, George Lansbury, Laurence Housman and Donald Soper; hearing them speak caused her hastily to revise what she now knew would have been her "discordant" contribution, as she found herself "more and more sympathetic with the complete pacifist outlook".

Far from simply celebrating the end of a war, the peace movement had much work to do. Military service legislation remained in force until the formal end of the whole British WW1 apparatus (eventually defined as 31 August 1921): so conscription continued, with some conscientious objectors still in prison, others on the Home Office Scheme, and others again serving in the Non-Combatant Corps (NCC) – some in France. The British government controversially but briefly equivocated over extending conscription long-term. Nevertheless, COs began to be released from prison before completion of their sentences, so that most had gone by April 1919, and the final few serving later sentences were released by August 1919. The Home Office Scheme was also wound up by April 1919, such COs likewise going home. For men in the NCC, demobilisation was in parallel with ordinary conscript soldiers, with the last not discharged until early 1920.

In reckoning, immediately after the war, the human cost of the British CO struggle, it was understood that some 16,000 men had resisted, whether as absolutists or alternativists; recent research has now increased the overall estimate to 20,000, with more than 18,000 already identified. Some 6000 had been imprisoned, for periods between a few months and three years, often including more than one sentence; and 35 were formally sentenced to death in 1916, though immediately reprieved. Commutation of such sentences to ten years' penal servitude was further commuted to time served, as part of the general release in April 1919. Although no British CO was executed, seventy names of COs known to have died in various ways, ten in prison, nine in Home Office Work Centres, others at home, often after premature release, were recorded on a plaque made in 1923 (the moving story behind this was told in the feature pages of the 2016 *Peace Diary*). Further research has increased the number known to have died to more than 100, including a few members of the Friends' Ambulance Unit killed by stray firing near the front line.

Plaque commemorating British COs who died because of their treatment during WW1

With the end of conscription, the No-Conscription Fellowship dissolved itself in early 1920, but by the following year core members realised an ongoing need for organised opposition to war and preparations for war, and founded the No More War Movement (NMWM), on 24 February 1921. The name was derived from the slogan, **No More War!**, **Plus Jamais la Guerre!**, **Nie Wieder Krieg!**, which marked demonstrations which began to be held annually in London, Berlin, and other capitals in July or August, marking anniversaries of the beginning of WW1. The NMWM soon became the first British affiliate of War Resisters' International, a federation of pacifist and conscientious objector organisations in many countries, which was founded by a small gathering of European conscientious objectors at Bilthoven, Netherlands, on 23 March 1921; it originally took the name Paco, Esperanto for "Peace", reflecting an overlap in international understanding between Esperantist and anti-war movements. In 1923 the name was changed in conscious alignment with the Socialist and Communist Internationals, but crucially declaring permanent rejection of war – which it declared "a crime against humanity".

Alongside the WRI there had been established on 9 October 1919, also at Bilthoven, the International Fellowship of Reconciliation (originally called the Movement towards a Christian International), linking FoR groups in many countries following the founding of British FoR in 1914. There was also the Women's International League for Peace and Freedom, established on 19 May 1919 at a conference in Zurich, Switzerland, complementing the International Congress of Women at the Hague in 1915, in the midst of war. (For more of the history of this movement, see the feature pages in the 2015 *Peace Diary*.)

Although performing even humanitarian service, if part of the war machine, has always been rejected by absolutist objectors and often accepted only reluctantly by alternativists, completely voluntary rescue and rehabilitation service through civilian agencies has regularly been seen as a constructive expression of pacifism during – and in the aftermath of – war and conflict. So a number of anti-war activists, many of them Quakers, went to Germany, Austria, Poland and Russia in the immediate post-war years to help with reconstruction among the physical debris and social chaos resulting from war. A further development of this kind of activity was the founding in 1931 of International Voluntary Service for Peace, a network of (mainly young) people in many countries willing to share in short-term work projects in other countries. They simultaneously provided (and still do provide) a useful service for a local community and – by bringing together, and reconciling, people of differing nationalities, cultures and languages – help to break down the suspicions, animosities and mistrust that have so often allowed war to happen or continue. Such work, by IVSP and other groups, became important again in the aftermath of the Second World War, and played a notable part in reconciliation between the communities in Northern Ireland in the 1960s–90s.

...and movements organise

The pressing concern of the conscientious objector movements emerging in countries across Europe was the prevalence of military conscription dating from the Napoleonic era – almost invariably without a right of conscientious objection. COs were often sentenced to lengthy or repeated terms of imprisonment: one French CO served twenty years on the notorious Devil's Island off the coast of French Guiana. The WRI was able to publicise such cases, although such publicity did little to embarrass the offending governments.

In totalitarian states such as Nazi Germany, Fascist Italy, Francoist Spain, the Soviet Union, and military-dominated parts of Latin America, genuine anti-militarist movements were simply illegal.

A little remembered interlude within the Versailles Treaty discussions was a proposal by Jan Smuts, Boer general during the South African War 1899–1902 but reconciled with the British sufficiently to become South African Prime Minister. He saw "conscription as the taproot of militarism; unless this is cut, all our labours will be in vain. Of ... proposals for disarmament the abolition of conscription is by far the most important." This was taken up by Woodrow Wilson, US President, and, with British co-operation, written into drafts for the League of Nations. But it was effectively vetoed by the Italian Prime Minister, Vittorio Orlando, because it would penalise poorer states, such as Italy, who could not afford a rate of pay sufficient to attract many volunteers. France also opposed abolition, claiming that compulsory military service was "a fundamental principle of democracy ... a corollary of universal suffrage". The whole question of abolition was simply abandoned within the discussions over the Versailles Treaty and the League of Nations.

But it was not forgotten. In August 1926 an ad hoc committee, under the auspices of the WRI, published a Manifesto against Conscription – signed by Norman Angell, Margaret Bondfield, Albert Einstein, Mohandas Gandhi, George Lansbury, Marian Parmoor, Romain

Rolland, and HG Wells, among others: "We ask the League of Nations to propose as the first step towards real disarmament the abolition of military conscription. We are convinced that armies based on conscription are a serious threat to peace ... Compulsory service means degradation to an obedience to commands; the whole system of training people to kill undermines respect for human personality, for democracy and for human life ... It inculcates a militarist spirit into the whole male population at a most impressionable age ... Thus war comes to be seen as inevitable, even as desirable."

Issued in twenty languages, the Manifesto was published simultaneously in virtually every country having a free press; but comment was mainly hostile; although a Joint Peace Council was established in 1928 to coordinate work of national bodies, the issue was not seriously taken up anywhere outside the radical peace movement. An attempt by the Council to revive the Manifesto in 1930, with further names, including Jane Addams, aroused much less interest.

Meanwhile, in October 1925 Arthur Ponsonby – the British MP who served as Under-Secretary at the Foreign Office in the first two Labour governments – invited people to sign a Peace Letter, saying, "We, convinced that all disputes between nations are capable of settlement either by diplomatic negotiations or by some form of international arbitration, hereby solemnly declare that we shall refuse to support or render war service to any Government which resorts to arms". A 9000-strong rally at London's Albert Hall on 5 December 1926, originally intended as the culmination of the campaign, served to boost further signatories, until letters signed by 128,770 people were presented to Prime Minister Stanley Baldwin on 8 December 1927. Yet more letters were handed in later.

The declared refusal by signatories of the Peace Letter to support any government resorting to arms was theoretically echoed by the British and many other governments who signed the Treaty of Paris on 27 August 1928. This initiative of Aristide Briand, some-time French premier, and Frank Kellogg, US Secretary of State, formally declared that the Treaty signatories – most of the major states – "condemn recourse to war for the solution of international controversies". But, unlike the Peace Letter signatories, they only "con-demned" and did not overtly refuse to resort to arms. The No More War Movement pointed out that the context of the Treaty – French support for Britain's claim for an enhanced navy, and British commitment that any disarmament agreement would not interfere with the French conscription system – made the Kellogg-Briand Pact a "diplomatic sham".

In 1933, with a post-WW1 generation of youth coming to maturity while war and armaments were increasingly in the news, the Oxford Union (the University debating society) debated the motion, "This House will in no circumstances fight for its King and Country"; it was carried by 275 votes to 153. Despite the declaration's purely symbolic nature, politicians and the press ful-minated as if the world had come to end, and there was even – unsuccessful – pressure put on the Union to expunge the resolution from the records.

Remembering differently

In 1933 also, another critique of militarism crystallised. Whereas in the early post-WW1 years the pacifist and conscientious objection movement had focussed, in terms of annual commemoration, on July and August anniversaries of the beginning of the war – and on the political atmosphere of chauvinism and patriotism that fuelled it – the annual state ceremonies from 1919 focussed on the end of the war, 11 November.

For a period, the British official commemorations remembered especially the *celebrations* at the war's conclusion, to the extent of holding further annual celebratory events. In 1925 Dick Sheppard, later founder of the Peace Pledge Union, wrote to *The*

Times that the plan to hold (in London's Albert Hall) on the evening of Armistice Day "a fancy dress ball on a vast scale as a tribute [following] the unspeakable agony of 1914–18 seems to me not so much irreligious as indecent".

Sheppard's letter resonated sufficiently for the ball to be cancelled, with a simple but solemn Service of Remembrance, conducted by Dick Sheppard, held instead. Afterwards, he wrote on his copy of the service sheet, "Of course, Pacifism must be written into this." The service has continued annually ever since, transposed to the evening before Remembrance Sunday, as Armistice Day has become. But so far from pacifism being written into it, the event is overlaid with military displays and militarist music, and weapons manufacturers subsidise the programme by advertising themselves and – implicitly – their latest means of destruction and murder.

The following year, in 1926, a letter to *No More War*, the NMWM paper, suggested that "To make Armistice Day a real Peace Day every poppy or other flower should bear the motto **No More War!**. If the British Legion … will not consent to this, then friends of the No More War Movement should themselves arrange for the sale of flowers bearing the motto. Many persons would rather give twopence or more for a flower with the motto rather than a penny for a flower alone." The writer was drawing attention to what had become a symbol for British WW1 Remembrance: the red poppy, which had grown profusely amid the mud and mayhem of the trenches. The symbol had been popularised through a

REMEMBRANCE
another view

THE
GLORIOUS
DEAD

PEACE PLEDGE UNION

poem by a Canadian military doctor, John McCrae: *In Flanders fields the poppies blow*. This poem not only focuses directly on the Allied military dead, to the exclusion of any other war dead, but also, by the injunction to the reader, "Take up our quarrel with the foe", explicitly urges perpetuation of killing; its frequent recitation in support of the red poppy makes clear the bellicosity and militarism represented by that poppy.

The letter to NMWM elicited no immediate response, but by 1933 members of the Women's Co-operative Guild (WCG) had come to a similar view and designed their own alternative poppy – white, instead of red. It had no space for "No More War!", but carried the more succinct "Peace". The red poppies are made in factories set up by the British Legion, the main organisation for military veterans, the factory workers being mainly disabled veterans; proceeds from the sale of red poppies support those incapacitated by war and dependants of those killed. (Of course, such support should be the moral responsibility of governments making wars.) The Women's Co-operative Guild invited the British Legion to make their white poppies on the same basis; but the Legion refused, so the Guild made their own.

The concept of the White Poppy, described by the WCG as "a pledge to peace that war must not happen again", was inclusive of all war dead – civilian or military, Allied or former enemy, killed directly by weapons or indirectly by the famine, disease and displacement inevitably associated with war. The idea spread across the peace movement, particularly in the newly launched Peace Pledge Union, from the mid-1930s. By 1937, with the support of Dick Sheppard, there developed the idea of a Remembrance event which would provide an alternative to the official ceremony at the Cenotaph in Whitehall, where wreaths of red poppies were laid. Instead, white poppy wreaths were laid in Regents Park. Sales of white poppies rose annually to a peak of 80,000 in 1938, despite cases of people being sacked for wearing them at work.

Pacifists face up to another war

The Peace Pledge Union had come about as part of the same foreboding of war in the early 1930s that gave rise to the Oxford Union resolution and the White Poppy. Dick Sheppard, a charismatic priest whose service as an Army chaplain in WW1 had led him to pacifism, published a letter in the *Guardian* and other papers on 16 October 1934, pronouncing that "war of every kind or for any cause is ... a crime against humanity", and inviting men to send him a postcard saying, "We renounce war and never again, directly or indirectly, will we support or sanction another".

Postcards arrived in tens of thousands and 7000 men came to an exploratory rally at the Albert Hall on 14 July 1935. Sheppard had not intended to set up another organisation, but groups began to spring up around the country, which on 22 May 1936 were formally coalesced into the Peace Pledge Union, the union of those who had made a solemn declaration against war and a commitment to peace. Although it had been thought important for men, as first candidates for any military call-up, to give that undertaking, it was quickly realised that women equally should be invited. Sheppard also made it clear from the outset that while he was motivated by his religion, the PPU was to be open to people of all faiths and none.

The numbers involved vastly outstripped the No More War Movement, with its similar same ethos and aims, and in February 1937 the NMWM formally merged into the PPU. Also, an independent initiative in north London, led by young journalist Humphrey Moore, established *Peace News,* "The only Weekly Newspaper serving all who are working for Peace" – first published on 6 June 1936. By mutual agreement, this soon became the paper of the PPU. *Peace News* separated from the PPU in 1961, along with Housmans Bookshop, founded by the PPU in 1945, with its *Peace Diary*, first issued in the 1954 edition.

Although the PPU and its paper were set up under the threat of another international war, it had a different war to face immediately – the Spanish Civil War. Many on the left in Britain sympathised with the government of the Republic against the extreme right-wing armed rebellion of Francisco Franco, and some volunteered for the International Brigade to support the Republic, but the WRI and PPU continued to affirm that if war was a crime against humanity, then that meant all wars. One major issue of impending war in the 1930s was targeted bombing of civilians, and it was necessary to point out that the horror of Guernica, perpetrated by German bombing planes on behalf of Franco, was an exemplar of what the RAF was preparing to do on other cities designated as "enemy" – as they were to go on to do in places such as Hamburg and Dresden. Yet rejecting warfare did not mean that there was nothing to be done. The PPU ran a house in Essex for 64 Basque refugee children, and the WRI ran a home for refugees in southern France.

When attempts failed to stop the Second World War before it even started, the PPU played a part in trying to stop some of its worst excesses, such as mass bombing

photo: Peace Pledge Union

The stone commemorating conscientious objectors in Tavistock Square, London: "To all those who have established and are maintaining the right to refuse to kill".

– or carpet bombing, as it was sometimes called, presumably in an effort to make it seem cosier. What Arthur Harris, head of Bomber Command, called "de-housing" (as if houses could be obliterated without reference to the children, women and men living there), Vera Brittain rightly called "methods of barbarism".

In another example, pacifism did not need to be passive. It was learned that partly because of Allied blockades, as well as the inevitable inefficiencies of running a militarily occupied country, some children in Europe, especially in Belgium and Greece, were starving. The PPU ran a Food Relief Campaign to work with the Red Cross to get food through; that work was a direct forerunner of Oxfam.

The revival of conscription in Britain from 1939 included provision for conscientious objection, the system operating much more fairly than in WW1: it was acknowledged that lessons had been learned. On the downside was the conscription of women, albeit relatively limited, and – what had been feared, but never realised, in WW1 – industrial conscription, for which there was no formal recognition of conscientious objection. Objecting to the whole state panoply of war was not seen by the authorities as morally the same as objecting specifically to combatant service. Altogether, there were some 60,000 objectors in WW2, including 1000 women; whereas 6000 COs were imprisoned in WW1, many for periods up to three years, the number imprisoned in WW2 was nearer 3000, mostly for months rather than years.

An important difference in the post-WW2 period, compared with the time after the First World War, was the continuation of male conscription until 1963, mostly for two years full-time followed by three-and-a-half years on the reserve (when you could be recalled annually for refresher service). There were some 10,000 more COs, but few hard cases. Conscientious objection to conscription however, has had one effect continuing to this day. In WW2 it was found necessary to devise a procedure for dealing with people who had either originally volunteered to join one of the armed forces, or who had originally accepted call-up without complaint, but, in either case, later developed a conscientious objection. A version of that procedure still exists in UK armed forces regulations for personnel who change their minds. It is not perfect, but it is there as a marker, and the USA is the only other state to have a fully comparable system for volunteer armed forces.

Struggles in a new era

With the launching of the Second World War, Remembrance became muted for militarists and war resisters alike. In the years after WW2 there were occasional minor revivals of the White Poppy until – in 1980 – London Peace Action, a spontaneous group loosely associated with the PPU, took up the concept more concertedly, linking it with laying a White Poppy wreath at the Cenotaph, separately from the State ceremony.

The PPU subsequently took over larger-scale production of White Poppies, which has continued ever since with sales eventually exceeding the 1938 high point of 80,000. More than 100,000 are now distributed annually. Laying a White Poppy wreath at the Cenotaph has been superseded by laying one at the Conscientious Objectors' Commemorative Stone in Tavistock Square in central London.

Another post-WW2 development, in terms of the commemorations of military events, related to the Atom Bomb, as it was called at the time of the unprecedented explosions over two Japanese cities – Hiroshima and Nagasaki – in 1945. The PPU published the first known leaflet against the Bomb, in November 1945, and organised the first public meeting about it, on 16 March 1946. But the focus on 6 August as the anniversary of the first use of the weapon on Hiroshima did not start until 1948, when it began to be called World Peace Day, with a focus on peace rather than war; the name lingered until 1951. An attempt to call it "No More Hiroshimas Day", shortened to Hiroshima Day, began in 1949, but did not really take off until 1961, well into the first phase of the specific nuclear disarmament movement.

The movement got seriously under way with the Direct Action Committee against Nuclear War (DAC), founded in 1957, and the Campaign for Nuclear Disarmament (CND), launched in 1958. That first wave of the nuclear disarmament movement has also left a legacy in the nuclear disarmament (ND) symbol designed by conscientious objector Gerald Holtom: the superimposed sema-phore symbols for N and D enclosed within a circle representing the world. The symbol was originally designed for DAC, for use on the first Aldermaston March (which DAC was organising for Easter weekend 1958). It quickly came to be adopted by other nuclear disar-mament campaigners, and has since become widely seen – especially beyond the UK – as a more general Peace Sign.

ATOM WAR

" A scientist told me that it would be quite easy to make an atomic bomb a thousand times as powerful as the first, which would make short work of London."

"It is not beyond imagination that a hundred tourists should leave a hundred suitcases in railway stations and a hun-dred cities would simply cease to be."

P. J. NOEL-BAKER, Minister-of-State
10th October, 1945.

As with the early post-WW1 commemorations on the anniversary of that war, commemorations of war – on whatever date, and in whichever era – lack meaning and significance unless they include a firm resolve to do

Gerald Holtom's early sketch for the nuclear disarmament symbol

everything possible to prevent future wars. One step is total disarmament, and total disarmament necessarily includes total abolition of armies, air forces and non-merchant navies.

In the later decades of the 20th century there were some small moves in the right direction. One by one, states in Europe began to modify conscription by recognising conscientious objection, often after long struggles in which lone COs had suffered obloquy and imprisonment. Towards the end of the century many states began to abolish conscription completely, though it is still avidly retained by some, such as Greece and Switzerland (famously untouched by war since 1815). Norway, perversely, has extended conscription to women, and Sweden (also untouched by war since 1815) has recently reintroduced conscription, having earlier abolished it, and also extended it to women. Turkey, with its ambivalent attitude towards human rights, firmly retains conscription, with little regard for conscientious objection. Israel also retains conscription, long extended to women. Ex-Soviet satellite Georgia abolished conscription not long ago, but very soon re-introduced it.

Shall we ever learn?

Looking back at the century of war resistance since WW1, progress has been mixed, at best. In Britain, the 1930s didn't just give rise to, for example, White Poppies and the PPU; it was also a time when genuine "card-carrying pacifists" could be major political leaders. PPU member George Lansbury was Leader of the Opposition in the House of Commons, and fellow member Arthur Ponsonby was Leader of the Opposition in the House of Lords. For most of the time since then, such a situation has been unthinkable.

In the decades after WW2, it was sometimes other, non-pacifist, peace movement struggles which gave a boost to the pacifist movement and the re-thinking of Remembrance. This was true of both the first wave of the nuclear disarmament movement in the late 1950s, and – especially – of the surge in the peace movement during the second anti-nuclear wave in the 1980s. This coincided with – and helped bring about – a revival of the White Poppy and a rethinking of Remembrance.

Yet the 1980s also saw an event where the pacifist and war resistance end of the British peace movement could feel a lonely place: the Falklands War. Here was a conflict that was not only popular with almost all of the wider public (as can so often be the case at the time a war is happening – providing it's fairly short, and far away), but one which many non-pacifist peace organisations found hard to oppose.

However, in this current era of an extended WW1 centenary period, a pacifist stance – and anti-militarist perspectives on Remembrance – are finding a strong echo not just within the wider movement, but amongst the public at large, as the failure of warfare to solve problems is increasingly apparent. War in the Balkans is a recent memory, and Middle East conflicts continue – both recurrences of disputes exacerbated by, not settled by, WW1.

Similarly, the Far East was not settled by the Second World War, with war in Korea starting only five years after WW2 ended; and sixty years later the Korean armistice is still only an armistice, with threats and counter-threats repeatedly dominating the news.

Sometimes, with long-enough hindsight, even many who are far from being pacifists now accept campaigners' critiques of WW1. So the time is ripe, during this centenary, for those of us opposing war to point to the visions of our predecessors. We must insist that the different course that could and should have been taken a hundred years ago is as relevant as ever. It has never been more important to turn away from the acceptance of officially sanctioned, organised slaughter.

A century on from the First World War, with so much still to do, we ask the same question:
When shall we ever learn?

January

The Community shall have as its task, by establishing a common market and progressively approximating the economic policies of Member States, to promote throughout the Community a harmonious development of economic activities, a continuous and balanced expansion, an increase in stability, an accelerated raising of the standard of living and closer relations between the States belonging to it.

Treaty of Rome, 1957, Article 2

WEEK I

MON

NEW YEAR'S DAY
(HOL UK/IRE/CAN/US)
WORLD PEACE DAY

I

1958 - Treaty establishing European Economic Community comes into force

TUE

○
(HOL SCOT)

2

1943 - Germany begins withdrawal from Caucasus, USSR

WED

3

1938 - Government announces gas masks for schoolchildren, Britain

THU

4

1978 - Augusto
Pinochet manipulates
plebiscite to shore
up dictatorship, Chile

FRI

5

1548 - Francesco
Suarez, pioneer of
international law,
born, Grenada, Spain

SAT

6

1878 - Marian
Parmoor, pacifist
activist, born, Britain

SUN

7

1993 - EU
investigation reports
up to 20,000 women
raped as strategy by
Bosnian Serbs

January

Lately a word has been carved for us on a Swiss chalet, to which we can hold and which significantly puts the joy first: En haut les coeurs; à bas les armes – *Lift up your hearts; lay down your weapons.*

Michael Tippett, *Abundance of Creation*, 1944

MON

8

1998 - Death of
Michael Tippett,
pacifist composer,
Britain

TUE

9

1988 - Women in
Black begin regular
vigil against
militarism of
government, Israel

WED

10

1983 - Public
enquiry opens on
proposed nuclear
power station B,
Sizewell, Britain

11

1908 - Gandhi
gaoled first time (2
months for refusing
to register as
Asiatic),
Johannesburg,
S Africa

12

1968 - Dissidents
Yuri Galanskov &
Alexander Ginsburg
sentenced to hard
labour, Moscow,
USSR

13

1958 - Petition to
UN for end of
nuclear weapons
tests signed by 2000
scientists from 44
countries

14

1943 - UK/USA
agree policy requir-
ing unconditional
surrender by
Germany & Japan,
summit conference,
Casablanca, Morocco

You cannot have a broader basis for any government than that which includes all the people, with all their rights in their hands, and with an equal power to maintain their rights.

William Lloyd Garrison

WEEK 3

MON

15

MARTIN LUTHER KING DAY
(HOL US)

1968 - "Jeanette Rankin Brigade" marches against Vietnam War, Washington DC, USA

TUE

16

1958 - National Committee for Abolition of Nuclear Weapons Tests dissolves into CND, London, Britain

WED

17

●

1968 - In protest against Vietnam war, Eartha Kitt disrupts luncheon, White House, Washington DC, USA

THU

18

1978 - UK found
guilty of inhuman &
degrading treatment
of prisoners in
N Ireland, ECHR,
Strasbourg

FRI

19

1978 - Government
cancels arms sales to
El Salvador, Britain

SAT

20

1993 - After decade
as refugees, 2500
Guatemalans return
from Mexico

SUN

21

1838 - William Lloyd
Garrison, nonviolent
activist, born,
Boston, USA

January

The Campaign for Nuclear Disarmament seeks to persuade people that atomic and similar armaments are totally wrong and should be abolished. One nation able to produce these weapons should set other nations an example by deliberately challenging the hysterical fear that is behind the arms race.

CND Statement of Policy [written by JB Priestley], 1958

MON

22

1918 - Because of shortages, government orders restaurants not to serve meat on two days each week, Britain

TUE

23

1978 - 2-week strike against Somoza dictatorship begins, Nicaragua

WED

24

1978 - Nuclear-powered Soviet satellite crashes, Canada

THU

25

1998 - 11 killed by
Tamil Tiger suicide
bombers, Kandy,
Sri Lanka

FRI

26

1828 - 1st Duke of
Wellington becomes
country's only
professional soldier
prime minister,
Britain

HOLOCAUST MEMORIAL DAY

SAT

27

1958 - Campaign for
Nuclear
Disarmament
launched, Britain

SUN

28

1918 - Bolsheviks
issue decree
founding Red Army,
Russia

January ∽ February

If the State wishes that its citizens respect human life, then the State should stop killing.
Clarence Darrow, attorney for the undefended, USA

MON

29

1928 - Treaty between Germany & Lithuania provides for arbitration over Memel

TUE

30

1948 - Mohandas Gandhi assassinated, Delhi, India

WED

31

1943 - German commander surrenders to Red Army, Stalingrad, USSR

THU

1

1948 - Communist
Party begins guerilla
war against
government, Malaya

FRI

2

1998 - Declaration
to reduce nuclear
weapons signed by
over 100 world
leaders

SAT

3

1998 - First
execution of woman
in state since 1860s,
Texas, USA

SUN

4

1938 - Adolf Hitler
declares himself
Army C-in-C,
Germany

February

The job of the peacemaker is to stop war, to purify the world, to get it saved from poverty and riches, to heal the sick, to comfort the sad … to create beauty and joy wherever you go.

Muriel Lester

WEEK 6

MON

5

1988 - Dictator Manuel Noriega charged with drug trafficking, leading to downfall & imprisonment, Panama

TUE

6

1998 - 9 killed by Tamil Tiger suicide bomber, Colombo, Sri Lanka

WED

7

1978 - Centre for Alternative Industrial & Technological Systems set up, London, Britain

THU

8

1988 - Withdrawal of troops from Afghanistan announced by USSR

FRI

9

1988 - Thousands demonstrate against Sandinista conscription, Masaya, Nicaragua

SAT

10

1918 - Russia signs peace with Germany

SUN

11

1968 - Death of Muriel Lester, Christian pacifist, Britain

February

We grew up in a state in which all free expression of opinion is unscrupulously repressed. The Hitler Youth, the SA and the SS have tried to stupefy us, subvert us, in the brightest years of our lives. We want genuine learning, real freedom of opinion.

"White Rose" leaflet, for distributing which Hans and Sophie Scholl were beheaded, Munich, 22 February 1943

WEEK 7

MON

12

1938 - In meeting with Adolf Hitler, Austrian Chancellor submits to Nazi control, Berchtesgaden, Bavaria, Germany

TUE

13

1968 - 5 soldiers arrested at pray-in for peace, Fort Jackson, S Carolina, USA

WED

14

1938 - Britain opens naval base, Singapore

THU
15
2003 - Millions
march worldwide
against war on Iraq

YUAN TAN
(CHINESE NEW YEAR 4716)

FRI
16
1993 - 8 Nobel
Peace laureates urge
release of Aung San
Suu Kyi by regime in
Burma

SAT
17
1958 - 5000 at first
public meetings of
CND, Methodist
Central Hall &
elsewhere, London,
Britain

SUN
18
1943 - Hans and
Sophie Scholl
distribute "White
Rose" leaflets at
University, Munich,
Germany

February

Liberty trains for liberty. Responsibility is the first step in responsibility.

William Edward Burghardt du Bois, *John Brown*, 1909

MON

19

PRESIDENTS' DAY
(HOL US)

1991 - 6000 rally
against Gulf War,
Brisbane, Australia

TUE

20

1943 - Hans and
Sophie Scholl
arrested for
distributing "White
Rose" leaflets.
Munich, Germany

WED

21

1948 - President
Eduard Benes
denounces
threatened
Communist
totalitarian takeover,
Czechoslovakia

THU

22

1943 - Hans and Sophie Scholl, nonviolent resisters to Nazis, beheaded, Germany

FRI

23

1868 - WEB du Bois, co-founder of NAACP, born, USA

SAT

24

1978 - Final document on Law of the Sea approved by UN Conference, Geneva, Switzerland

SUN

25

1988 - USSR withdraws SS-12 missiles from E Germany & Czechoslovakia

February ❧ March

No man is an island entire of itself ... any man's death diminishes me, because I am involved in mankind, therefore never send to know for whom the bell tolls; it tolls for thee.

John Donne

MON

26

1993 - Bomb explodes at World Trade Center, New York, USA

TUE

27

1998 - Cease-fire declared in civil war, Cambodia

WED

28

1988 - 80,000 demonstrate against nuclear power, Brokdorf, W Germany

THU

1

1943 - Mass rally
calls on government
to offer sanctuary to
Jewish refugees,
Madison Square,
New York, USA

FRI

2

1916 - Military
conscription, with
right of
conscientious
objection, comes
into force, Britain

SAT

3

1918 - Treaty ending
war between Soviet
Russia and Germany
signed, Brest-Litovsk,
Russia

SUN

4

1978 - 40,000
demonstrate against
construction of
uranium enrichment
plant, Almelo,
Netherlands

March

What is the arms race and the cold war but the continuation of male competitiveness and aggression into the inhuman sphere of computer-run institutions? If women are to cease producing cannon-fodder for the final holocaust, they must rescue men from the perversities of their own polarisation.

Germaine Greer, *The Female Eunuch*, 1970

MON

5

1988 -
Demonstrations
against "nuclear
mafia", Essen,
Gorleben, Frankfurt
& Regensburg,
W Germany

TUE

6

1928 - Communist
raid leaves reported
3000 dead, Beijing,
China

WED

7

1988 - Federal court
rules for same
access to schools by
peace groups as by
military, USA

THU

8

1908 - Strike by
garment workers,
USA: leads to
International
Women's Day

FRI

9

1968 - 500 march
against impending
launch of 4th Polaris
submarine,
Birkenhead, Britain

SAT

10

1968 - "Close all
bases" campaign
begins with
leafletting USAF
Lakenheath, Suffolk,
Britain

SUN

11

1958 - Plane
accidentally drops
nuclear weapon
(without explosion),
Mars Bluff,
S Carolina, USA

March

It is organised violence on top which creates individual violence at the bottom.

Emma Goldman

MON

12

1978 - 150,000 demonstrate against nuclear reactor, Lemoniz, Spain

TUE

13

1938 - *Anschluss*: annexation of Austria by Germany

WED

14

1978 - 50,000 march against construction of uranium enrichment plant, Almelo, Netherlands

1968 - 6 protesters
ejected from
shipyard at launch of
UK's 4th Polaris
submarine,
Birkenhead, Britain

1968 - Massacre by
US troops of 500
unarmed women &
children, My Lai,
S Vietnam

●
ST PATRICK'S DAY
(HOL NI/IRE)

1948 - Treaty
originating Western
European Union
signed, Brussels,
Belgium

1918 - First
governmental plan
for a League of
Nations proposed by
UK

March

There can be no peace so long as hunger and want are found among millions of working people and the few, who make up the employing class, have all the good things of life.

Industrial Workers of the World ("The Wobblies"), Preamble to founding document, 1905

WEEK 12

MON
19

1978 - 50,000 march against neutron bomb, Amsterdam, Netherlands

TUE

EQUINOX

20

1948 - USSR withdraws from Allied Control Commission for Germany

WED
21

1978 - Israel calls cease-fire, Lebanon

SAKA
(INDIAN NEW YEAR 1940)

THU

22

1958 - Women
demonstrate against
pass laws, S Africa

FRI

23

1918 - Trial opens of
101 IWW members
for opposing WW1,
USA

SAT

24

1948 - Charter of
International Trade
Organisation signed

BST BEGINS

SUN

25

1967 - Walk for
Peace to Pentagon
leaves Boston,
Massachusetts, USA

March ～ April

To all those who call me traitor, I say that I am proud and happy to have done what I did. I am glad that I succeeded. All the secrets were published and are in the hands of the whole world. I am now ready to start my life.

Mordechai Vanunu, on release from 16 years in Ashkelon Prison, Israel, 21 April 2004

WEEK 13

MON

26

1978 - 500 fast against construction of nuclear reactors, Switzerland

TUE

27

1988 - Mordechai Vanunu gaoled 18 years for disclosing nuclear weapons programme, Israel

WED

28

1858 - Aylmer Maude, interpreter of Tolstoy, born, Britain

29

1987 - Vietnam
Veterans for Peace
marching from
Jinotega reach
Wicuili, Nicaragua

GOOD FRIDAY
(HOL UK/CAN)

30

1928 - Non-fascist
youth movements
ordered to be
disbanded, Italy

○

31

1998 - Air force
permanently with-
draws nuclear bombs
from service, Britain

EASTER DAY

1

1918 - Royal Air
Force established,
UK

April

I may not get there with you, but I want you to know tonight that we as a people will get to the promised land. So, I'm happy tonight, I'm not worried about anything, I'm not fearing any man. Mine eyes have seen the glory...

Martin Luther King, Memphis, 3 April 1968, the evening before his assassination

MON

EASTER MONDAY
(HOL ENG/W/NI/IRE/CAN)

2

1908 - 35 killed in collision between two RN ships, off Isle of Wight, Britain

TUE

3

1968 - The night before his assassination Martin Luther King urges his people on to "the promised land", Memphis, Tennessee, USA

WED

4

1958 - 4000 begin first march to Aldermaston AWRE from Trafalgar Square, London, Britain

5

1948 - First
shipment of Marshall
Aid for Europe
leaves USA

6

1998 - Medium
range missile test-
fired, Pakistan

7

1948 - World Health
Organisation
founded, Geneva,
Switzerland

8

1993 - Women in
Black demonstrate in
solidarity with their
Serbian sisters, Lund,
Sweden

April

*If Negro freedom is taken away, or that of any minority group,
the freedom of all people is taken away.*

Paul Robeson

MON

9

1898 - Paul
Robeson, radical
singer and actor,
born, Princeton,
New Jersey, USA

TUE

10

1998 - After 30
years of conflict,
parties agree on
settlement, N Ireland

WED

11

1968 - Anti-
discriminatory Civil
Rights Act comes
into force, USA

THU
12
1993 - NATO begins enforcing "no-fly" zone, Bosnia

FRI
13
1928 - US Secretary of State Frank Kellogg submits plan for abolishing war to Locarno powers

SAT
14
1988 - Ports declared nuclear-free, Denmark

WAR TAX RESISTANCE DAY (US)

SUN
15
1993 - 1040 Resisters celebrate Tax Day by burning tax forms, Bangor, Maine, USA

April

Nonviolence is really tough. You don't practise nonviolence by attending conferences – you practise it on the picket lines.
Cesar Chavez

●

MON

16

1948 - Organisation for European Economic Co-operation established

TUE

17

1968 - 20,000 in final rally of Aldermaston March, Trafalgar Square, London, Britain

WED

18

1958 - First march against nuclear arms, W Germany

19

1948 - Army formally
disbanded, Costa
Rica

20

1993 - Women in
Black demonstrate in
solidarity with their
Serbian sisters,
Vienna, Austria

21

1898 - USA declares
war on Spain

22

1993 - Bill for
unilateral
disarmament tabled
in Senate, France

April

My socialism is based on belief in the sacredness of all human life… If this belief is to find expression in modern civilisation, the social order must be reconstructed to encourage what is best in human life instead of degrading it.

Fenner Brockway, Statement to Military Service Tribunal, 1916

WEEK 17

MON
23
1993 - Death of
Cesar Chavez,
nonviolent activist,
USA

TUE
24
1938 - At instigation
of Adolf Hitler,
Konrad Henlein
demands autonomy
for Sudetenland,
Czechoslovakia

WED
ANZAC DAY (AUS)
25
1938 - UK settles
outstanding disputes
with Irish Free State

26

1993 - Women in
Black demonstrate in
solidarity with their
Serbian sisters,
Toronto, Canada

27

1939 -
Re-introduction of
military conscription
approved in principle
by Parliament, Britain

28

1988 - Death of
Fenner Brockway,
peace campaigner,
Britain

29

1968 - Death of
Theodor
Michaltscheff, co-
founder of IdK,
Bulgaria

April ❧ May

The hellish instruments of war must be smoked out while there is still peace… The trade unions must be compelled not to allow their old resolutions to fade in the files; and they will have to go far beyond their old resolutions.

Carl von Ossietzky, *Die Weltbühne*, 19 February 1929

MON

30

1977 - 2000 occupy nuclear power plant, Seabrook, New Hampshire, USA

TUE

1

1958 - Crew of *Golden Rule* arrested by US Navy in nuclear test area, Pacific

WED

2

1998 - Silent marches outside 8 gunmakers' headquarters, USA

THU

3

1938 - Adolf Hitler
ceremonially
received by Benito
Mussolini, Rome,
Italy

FRI

4

1938 - Death of Carl
von Ossietzky, Nobel
Peace laureate,
Berlin, Germany

SAT

5

1993 -
Dhammayietra II to
Pnom Penh leaves
Siem Reap,
Cambodia

SUN

6

1993 - UN Security
Council declares safe
areas in Bosnia-
Herzegovina

May

CHRISTIAN AID WEEK, 14–19 May

Christian Aid is the aid and development wing of the Council of Churches in Britain. The week focuses on the need for helping the self-development and achievement of justice of people enduring poverty, famine and war in many parts of the world.
Contact: Christian Aid, 35 Lower Marsh, Waterloo, London SE1 7RL, Britain; tel +44-20-7620 4444; www.christianaid.org.uk

WEEK 19

MON

7

MAY DAY OBSERVED
(HOL UK/IRE)

1918 - Treaty signed ending war between Romania and Central Powers

TUE

8

◗

1958 - US Secretary of State declares attack on Berlin would be regarded as attack on Western Allies, W Berlin

WED

9

1993 - Network for deserters and COs from former Yugoslavia established, Salzburg, Austria

10

1968 - "Night of the
Barricades" as
government con-
cedes some student
demands, Paris,
France

11

1998 - Second series
of nuclear weapon
tests begun,
Rajasthan, India

12

1978 - Icelandic
gunboat attacks
British trawler,
Atlantic Ocean

13

1943 - Germany and
Italy surrender in
North Africa

May

There is no hope for an eradication of war but by an absolute and total abandonment of it.

Jonathan Dymond, *The Pacific Principles of the New Testament*

MON

14

1948 - Unilateral declaration of the State of Israel, Tel Aviv, Palestine

TUE

15

●

INT'L CONSCIENTIOUS
OBJECTORS' DAY

1988 - USSR begins withdrawal of troops from Afghanistan

WED

16

1828 - Death of Jonathan Dymond, peace activist, Britain

THU
17
1968 - Berrigan brothers & 7 others burn 600 military draft files, Catonsville, Maryland, USA

FRI
18
1978 - Yuri Orlov, human rights campaigner, sentenced to 7 years in labour camp, USSR

SAT
19
1918 - 44 killed in German air raid on London, Britain

SUN
20
1958 - Mass unilateral nuclear disarmament lobby of Parliament, London, Britain

May

Our apologies, good people, for the fracture of good order, the burning of paper instead of children, the angering of the orderlies in the front parlor of the charnel house.

Daniel Berrigan, on behalf of the Catonsville 9, Maryland, USA, 17 May 1968

WEEK 21

MON

21

1998 - President Raden Suharto resigns in response to people power, Indonesia

TUE

◑

22

2017 - 22 (including 7 children) killed in "Islamic State" bombing as concert closes, Arena, Manchester, Britain

WED

23

1978 - First UN Special Session on Disarmament opens, New York, USA

INT'L WOMEN'S DAY FOR
DISARMAMENT

THU

24

1968 - 4 gaoled for 6
years for pouring
blood on draft cards,
Baltimore, Maryland,
USA

FRI

25

1993 - UN War
Crimes Tribunal
created for
Yugoslavia

SAT

26

1988 - Thanassis
Makris gaoled 5
years as
conscientious
objector, Greece

SUN

27

1943 - National
Resistance Council
of politicians,
unionists & others
formed, France

May ∾ June

We have the instruments [of war] ... Who will confront this crime? ... Only the resisting people, those who confront weapons, weapons-makers, and their immaculate guardians – the law.
Philip Berrigan

MON

28

1998 - Series of
nuclear weapon tests
begins, Pakistan

MEMORIAL DAY (US)
(HOL UK/US)

TUE

29

1978 - Troops
massacre 100
campesinos
protesting against
eviction, Panzos, Alta
Vehapaz, Guatemala

○

WED

30

1998 - Global
Marches against
Child Labour
converge for rally,
Geneva, Switzerland

THU

31

1968 - President
Lyndon Johnson
announces
restriction of US
bombing of
N Vietnam

FRI

1

1993 - Police brutally
repress mass
demonstrations
against regime,
Serbia

SAT

2

1848 - Paul
Sveistrup, peace
activist, born,
Denmark

SUN

3

1938 - Law
authorises
confiscation of
"degenerate" art,
Germany

June

We should not overlook the courage required to face the odds that were against Tolstoy when he delivered his message. Arrayed against him were the Church, the State, the censor, the militarists, the patriots, all who sought honours, distinctions and material prosperity.

Aylmer Maude, Introduction to his translation of Tolstoy's *The Kingdom of God and Peace Essays*, 1936

WEEK 23

MON

4

INT'L DAY FOR CHILDREN AS
VICTIMS OF WAR
(HOL IRE)

1943 - Military coup
d'état, Argentina

TUE

5

1998 - Palais Wilson,
House for Human
Rights, dedicated,
Geneva, Switzerland

WED

6

◐

1993 - Guerillas
massacre 450 in
attack on refugee
camp, Harbel, Liberia

THU
7
1948 - France, UK & US agree programme for development of Western-occupied zones of Germany

FRI
8
1928 - Nationalist capture of Beijing ends civil war, China

SAT
9
1993 - Police ban vigil of Women in Black, Belgrade, Serbia

SUN
10
1958 - UN Commercial Arbitration Treaties signed

June

The greatest heroes of the world are not men who kill other men in war. They are the quiet heroes who are brave in other ways.

Rufus Jones

MON

11

1948 - UN Truce Team established, Palestine

TUE

12

1968 - UN General Assembly approves Nuclear Non-Proliferation Treaty, New York, USA

WED

13

1993 - UN "peacekeepers" shoot 14 unarmed demonstrators, Mogadishu, Somalia

THU

14

1988 - American-Soviet peace walk to San Francisco leaves Washington DC, USA

FRI

15

1943 - Congress of Racial Equality founded, Chicago, USA

SAT

16

1948 - Death of Rufus Jones, founding chair of AFSC, Haverford, Connecticut, USA

SUN

17

1918 - Food riots, Vienna, Austria

June

If it were proved to me that in making war, my ideal had a chance of being realised, I would still say "No" to war. For one does not create a humane society on mounds of corpses.

Louis Lecoin

MON

18

1778 - British troops
evacuated from
Philadelphia, USA

TUE

19

1988 - Military coup
d'état, Haiti

WED

20

1958 - Peace March
to Tokyo leaves
Hiroshima, Japan

THU

21

1788 - Sweden
declares war on
Russia

FRI

22

1958 - Star March is
CND's first major
demonstration,
London, Britain

SAT

23

1971 - Death of
Louis Lecoin, pacifist
activist, France

SUN

24

1948 - USSR
blockades road & rail
access from West
Germany to
W Berlin

June ∽ July

The right to refuse to kill.

The essence of conscientious objection to military service, as summed up on the CO Commemorative Stone, Tavistock Square, Bloomsbury, London.

MON

25

1993 - Armed Afrikaner Volksfront members storm talks on constitutional change, World Trade Centre, Johannesburg, S Africa

TUE

INT'L DAY FOR VICTIMS OF TORTURE

26

1998 - International Day in Support of Victims of Torture first observed

WED

27

1918 - Marie Equi, physician & anarchist, arrested for anti-war speech, Portland, Oregon, USA

THU

28

1988 - President
Mikhail Gorbachev
outlines *glasnost* &
perestroika,
Communist Party
Conference,
Moscow, USSR

FRI

29

1968 - 200 in token
occupation of USAF
base, Alconbury,
Britain

SAT

30

1968 - World
petition for
recognition of
conscientious
objection presented
to UN Human
Rights Commission

SUN

1

1948 - Allied airlift
to overcome Soviet
blockade of W Berlin
begins, W Germany

July

It has been argued that when killing is viewed as not only permissible but heroic behaviour, sanctioned by one's government or cause, the fine distinction between taking a human life and other forms of impermissible violence gets lost, and rape becomes an unfortunate and but inevitable by-product of the necessary game called war.

Susan Brownmiller, *Against Our Will: Men, Women and Rape*

WEEK 27

MON

CANADA DAY OBSERVED
(HOL CAN)

2

1968 - 30 arrested in
student
demonstration
against conscription,
Sydney, Australia

TUE

3

1988 - US warship
kills 290 civilians by
shooting down
Iranian aeroplane,
Persian Gulf

WED

INDEPENDENCE DAY
(HOL US)

4

1968 - 45 arrested
after mounted police
charge anti-Vietnam
War demonstrators,
US Consulate,
Melbourne, Australia

5

1938 - It is reported
that many Jews have
committed suicide in
recent days, Vienna,
Austria

6

1993 - Women for a
Nuclear Test Ban
climb over wall,
Buckingham Palace,
London, Britain

7

1918 - 50 girls killed
in German bombing
raid on hospital, La
Panne, Belgium

DAY OF COMMEMORATION (IRE)

8

1898 - May
Picqueray,
antimilitarist
anarchist, born,
Larzac, France

July

I stand against all learning, all institutions, all governments, all arts, all religions, which reject love. I oppose the politicians who rely on force and know nothing about love. If I have to be arrested for saying this, let me be handcuffed, for I would rather die quickly by the sword than die of thirst in a loveless desert.

Toyohiko Kagawa, *Love the Law of Life*, 1929

WEEK 28

MON

9

1998 - Statues of Martin Luther King and other Christian martyrs unveiled, Westminster Abbey, London, Britain

TUE

10

1888 - Toyohiko Kagawa, Christian pacifist, born, Japan

WED

11

1968 - American Indian Movement founded, Minneapolis, Minnesota, USA

(HOL NI)

THU

12

1998 - Three young
brothers killed in
Loyalist arson attack
on house,
Ballymoney,
Co Antrim, N Ireland

FRI

13

1948 - Ole Helga
Bakke is first
international civil
servant killed in
office, Palestine

SAT

14

1978 - Massacre by
guerillas of 17 black
villagers, Rhodesia

SUN

15

1958 - US invades
Lebanon

July

Man has no right to kill his brother. It is no excuse that he does so in uniform; he only adds the infamy of servitude to the crime of murder.

Percy Bysshe Shelley

MON

16

1968 - Five Warsaw Treaty states condemn Czechoslovak political reforms, Warsaw, Poland

TUE

17

1998 - Treaty establishing International Criminal Court for crimes against humanity approved by 120 states, Rome, Italy

WED

18

1998 - Truce declared between Chiapas rebels and government, Mexico

THU

19

2016 - Peace Tax Bill
introduced in House
of Commons,
London, Britain

FRI

20

1998 - In protest
against unequal
treatment of women,
EU suspends
humanitarian aid to
Taliban regime in
Afghanistan

SAT

21

1958 - 9-week picket
begins at
Aldermaston AWRE,
Berkshire, Britain

SUN

22

1998 - Medium-
range missile tested
by Iran

July

If one takes care of the means, the end will take care of itself …
We have always control over the means and never of the ends.
Mohandas Karamchand Gandhi

MON

23

1998 - 150 killed in
UNITA attack,
Angola

TUE

24

1988 - 10,000 form
human chain for a
cleaner North Sea,
W Germany

WED

25

1988 - David Bruce
gaoled for 6 years as
conscientious
objector, S Africa

26

1928 - Branch of
World Disarmament
Movement founded,
Melbourne, Australia

27

1968 - Alexander
Dubcek rejects
Warsaw Treaty
condemnation of
political reforms,
Prague,
Czechoslovakia

28

1868 - Black
Americans
recognised as
citizens, USA

29

1958 - National
Aeronautical and
Space Administration
created,
Washington DC,
USA

July ‿ August

*A good end cannot sanctify evil means, nor must we ever do evil
that good may come of it.*
William Penn

MON

30

1718 - Death of
William Penn,
Quaker pioneer,
Pennsylvania,
N America

TUE

31

1998 - Government
announces ban on
use of landmines by
its troops, Britain

WED

1

1943 - Declaration
of independence,
under Japanese
"protection", Burma

THU

2

1978 - Anglican
Pacifist Fellowship
nails invitation to
Bishops to debate
war, West Door,
Canterbury
Cathedral, Britain

FRI

3

1988 - 143 war
resisters publicly
refuse call-up,
S Africa

SAT

4

1837 - George
McNeill, nonviolent
international labour
arbitrator, born, USA

SUN

5

1992 - 100,000
march for multiracial
government, S Africa

August

Though I sit behind prison walls, I still believe that I can build further on your love and devotion in the days to come. And should I have to leave this life, I will still [rest easy in] my grave, for you know that I am not here as a criminal.

Franz Jägerstätter, writing from prison to his wife before his sentence and execution as a conscientious objector, 1943

WEEK 32

MON

HIROSHIMA DAY
(HOL SCOT/IRE)

6

1998 - 250,000 march against Indian & Pakistani nuclear tests, Calcutta, India

TUE

7

1998 - 240 killed in Islamic militant bombing of US embassies, Nairobi, Kenya, & Dar-es-Salaam, Tanzania

WED

8

1998 - Loyalist Volunteer Force announces permanent end to its violent campaign, N Ireland

THU

9

1943 - Austrian CO
Franz Jägerstätter
beheaded, Berlin,
Germany

FRI

10

1993 - 300 arrested
in protest against
rainforest clearance,
Clayoquot Sound,
British Columbia,
Canada

SAT

●

11

1943 - 21 COs
strike against prison
dining hall racial
segregation,
Danbury,
Connecticut, USA

SUN

12

1978 - 40 arrested
for scaling fence at
nuclear plant site,
Shoreham, New
York, USA

August

Hatred, which could destroy so much, never failed to destroy the man who hated, and this is an immutable law.

James Baldwin

MON

13

1978 - 100 killed by bomb, PLO HQ, Beirut, Lebanon

TUE

14

1976 - 10,000 in first demonstration of Peace People, Andersonstown, Belfast, Northern Ireland

WED

15

1928 - International Union of Antimilitarist Ministers and Clergy founded, Amsterdam, Netherlands

16

1928 - Military
conscription
re-introduced, USSR

17

1928 - World Youth
Peace Congress
opens, Eende,
Ommen,
Netherlands

18

1982 - After climbing
over closed Spanish
gate from Gibraltar,
13 nonviolent
activists deported
under armed escort
from Spain

19

1958 - NAACP
youth council begins
sit-ins to desegregate
lunch counters,
Oklahoma, USA

August

Resistance began in the early hours of the invasion. Employees of the government news agency refused orders to issue a release stating that certain officials had requested the takeover... the clandestine radio network called one-hour general strikes; requested rail workers to slow down transport of Russian jamming equipment; and discouraged collaboration within the State Police.

Beverley Woodward, *Czechoslovakia – 1968*, WRL Peace Calendar 1978

MON

20

1968 - Soviet
invasion met with
nonviolent
resistance,
Czechoslovakia

TUE

21

1991 - People power
overcomes
attempted coup
d'état, Moscow,
USSR

WED

22

1948 - Death of
Leyton Richards,
pacifist pastor, Britain

23

2008 - 2 boats from Cyprus bringing aid and international support break Israeli siege of Gaza harbour, Palestine

24

1958 - 6000 march for self-government, British Honduras

25

1948 - Central Committee for Conscientious Objectors founded, USA

26

1346 - English army introduces longbow and bombard to continental warfare, Crecy, France

August ∾ September

The High Contracting Parties solemnly declare in the names of their respective peoples that they condemn recourse to war for the solution of international controversies.

Treaty of Paris, 1928, Article 1

MON

27

1928 - Treaty for renunciation of war as national policy signed by major states, Paris, France

TUE

28

1828 - Leo Tolstoy, nonviolent novelist, born, Yasnaya Polyana, Russia

WED

29

1977 - First world conference on desertification, Nairobi, Kenya

30

1948 - Convention on Protection of Civilians in War signed, Stockholm, Sweden

31

1688 - Death of John Bunyan, prisoner of conscience, England

1

1988 - First Pershing II missiles are removed for destruction, W Europe

2

1993 - Women in Black demonstrate in solidarity with their Serbian sisters, Lancaster, Pennsylvania, USA

September

Even more disquieting than the actual practice of violence is the confidence people repose in it. This confidence has now become a real cult, a new religion.

Bart de Ligt, *The Conquest of Violence: An Essay on War and Revolution*

MON

◐
LABOUR DAY (HOL CAN/US)

3

1938 - Death of Bart de Ligt, nonviolence theorist, Netherlands

TUE

4

1878 - Ruth Fry, recorder of pacifism in action, born, Britain

WED

5

1798 - Military conscription ordained, France

6

1988 - 7 arrested in
protest at uranium
processing plant,
Fernwald, Ohio, USA

7

1948 - 3000 attend
launch of Peace
Council, Melbourne
Town Hall, Australia

8

1968 - 400 protest
at US arms depot,
Caerwent,
Monmouthshire,
Wales

●
ROSH HASHANAH
(JEWISH NEW YEAR 5779)

9

1968 - Committee
of 100 dissolves
itself, Britain

September

Science is telling us that we must have no lesser unit than the world. It is because we have been thinking in the outworn language of nationalism that disaster has overtaken us, for no country can live to itself alone any more than the hand or foot can live alone.

Ruth Fry, *Gleanings*, 1943

MON
10
1943 - German troops occupy Rome, Italy

TUE
11
1978 - Martial law declared, Nicaragua

MUHARRAM
(ISLAMIC NEW YEAR 1440)

WED
12
1968 - Albania withdraws from Warsaw Treaty

THU
13
1993 - Israel & PLO
sign peace accord,
Washington DC,
USA

FRI
14
1918 - Eugene Debs
gaoled 10 years for
alleged breach of
Espionage Act, USA

SAT
15
1943 - Rescued by
German troops,
Benito Mussolini
proclaims new
republic, Solo, Lake
Garda, Italy

SUN
16
1978 - Conscription
of blacks, on same
basis as whites,
announced, Rhodesia

September

While there is a lower class, I am in it; while there is a criminal element, I am of it; while there is a soul in prison, I am not free.

Eugene Victor Debs

MON

17

1978 - Egypt and Israel agree framework for peace, Camp David, USA

TUE

18

1838 - Peace convention opens, Boston, Massachusetts, USA

WED

19

1968 - Society of Teachers Opposed to Physical Punishment launched, Britain

20

1848 - Second
Universal Peace
Congress opens,
Brussels, Belgium

UN INT'L DAY OF PEACE

21

1988 - State of
emergency declared,
Naggorno-Karabakh,
USSR

22

1938 - PPU leaders
hand in demand for
peaceful solution of
Czechoslovak crisis,
Downing St, London,
Britain

EQUINOX
INT'L DAY OF PRAYER FOR PEACE

23

1993 - Parliament
votes in special
sitting to allow blacks
first ever share in
political power,
Pretoria, S Africa

September

End NATO! End the US war in Vietnam! End the occupation of Czechoslovakia!

The three slogans of the WRI Support Czechoslovakia actions, 1968

MON

24

1968 - WRI organises protests against Soviet invasion of Czechoslovakia: Budapest, Moscow, Sofia, Warsaw

TUE

25

○

1878 - Peace Congress, Paris, France

WED

26

1928 - General Act for peaceful settlement of disputes adopted by League of Nations, Geneva, Switzerland

THU

27

1993 - Salih
Askerogul arrested
as conscientious
objector, N Nicosia,
N Cyprus

FRI

28

1938 - Victor Jara,
singer of freedom,
born, Chile

SAT

29

1918 - Armistice
with Allies signed by
Bulgaria

SUN

30

1888 - Louis Lecoin,
pacifist activist, born,
France

October

When we pay our army and navy estimates, let us set down – so much for killing, so much for maiming, so much for making widows and orphans ... we shall by this means know what we have paid our money for.

Anna Laetitia Barbauld (1743–1825)

MON

1938 - German
troops march into
Sudetenland,
Czechoslovakia

TUE

◑
INT'L DAY OF NONVIOLENCE

2

1931 - Pope Pius XI
issues encyclical
urging disarmament,
Vatican

WED

3

1992 - Marchers
denounce
neo-Nazism,
Germany

THU

4

1982 - Ben Sasway,
first of new
generation of draft
resisters, gaoled,
USA

FRI

5

1968 - Death of
Frank Dawtry,
pacifist & penal
reformer, Britain

SAT

6

1978 - 346 arrested
at site of Black Fox
nuclear plant, Incla,
Oklahoma, USA

SUN

7

1957 - International
Atomic Energy
Agency established,
Vienna, Austria

October

The compelling motive for refusing to comply with the Draft Act is my uncompromising opposition to the principle of conscription of life by the State for any purpose whatever, in time of war or peace... I am the more opposed to the present act because it is for the purpose of conducting war. I am opposed to this and all other wars.

Roger Baldwin, statement to Court before being gaoled for 1 year, New York, USA, 1918

WEEK 41

MON

THANKSGIVING (CAN)
COLUMBUS DAY OBSERVED (US)
(HOL CAN/US)

8

1998 - Remorse for past expressed in treaty between S Korea and Japan

TUE

●

9

1918 - Roger Baldwin, co-founder of WRL, refuses military induction, USA

WED

10

1918 - 400 killed in German torpedoing of Irish mail-boat *Leinster*

11

1997 - Council of
Europe calls for
universal abolition of
death penalty

12

1978 - UN Centre
for Human
Settlements set up,
Nairobi, Kenya

13

1915 - 41 killed in
Zeppelin raid on
London

14

1992 - 3 pour blood
on Columbus statue
to mark 500 years of
genocide,
Washington DC,
USA

October

WEEK OF PRAYER FOR WORLD PEACE 14–21 OCTOBER

The week leading towards UN Day was established in 1974 as an opportunity for people of all faiths to focus on peace throughout the world.

Contact: Week of Prayer for World Peace, c/o 126 Manor Green Road, Epsom, Surrey, KT19 8LN, Britain; tel +44-1628-530309; www.weekofprayerforworldpeace.com

MON

15

1969 - Nuclear-
armed plane in air
collision, Kentucky,
USA

TUE

◐

16

1998 - Augusto
Pinochet arrested
for crimes under his
dictatorship in Chile,
London, Britain

WED

INT'L DAY FOR ERADICATION OF
POVERTY

17

1858 - Lydia
Wentworth, pacifist
writer, born,
Roxbury,
Massachusetts, USA

THU

18

1992 - Plaque
commemorating
Vietnam War
Resisters dedicated,
Washington Sq
Methodist Church,
New York, USA

FRI

19

1968 - Death of
Aldo Capitini,
co-founder of
Movimento
Nonviolento, Italy

SAT

20

1968 - Gonzalo Arias
arrested for *Los
Encartelados*
demonstration,
Madrid, Spain

SUN

21

1995 - 85,000 rally
for withdrawal of US
bases, Okinawa,
Japan

October

ONE WORLD WEEK 21–28 OCTOBER

Based on UN Day, One World Week is intended to encourage
people to link with international issues through taking up
overseas concerns in church, trade union, school etc.
Contact: One World Week, 35–39 London Street, Reading RG1
4PS, Britain; tel +44-118-939 4933; www.oneworldweek.org

WEEK 43

MON

22

1956 - Mass
demonstrations for
"democratic
reform", Hungary

TUE

23

1993 - IRA bomb
kills 9 in fish shop,
Shankill Road,
Belfast, Northern
Ireland

WED

○
UNITED NATIONS DAY

24

1648 - Thirty Years'
War ends with
Peace of Westphalia

25

1987 - France
conducts 88th
nuclear test,
Mururoa Atoll, Pacific

26

1991 - Tanks
destined for Israel
are discovered
labelled "agricultural
implements",
Hamburg harbour,
Germany

27

1967 - UN
terminates South
African mandate in
Namibia

BST ENDS

28

1989 - Police attack
10,000
demonstrators for
democracy, Prague,
Czechoslovakia

October ❦ November

Called for in the Final Document of the First UN Special Session
on Disarmament in 1978, Disarmament Week is a time for
pressing on all governments and arms manufacturers the urgent
need for disarmament of all kinds of weapons.
Contact: Your nearest national UNA

WEEK 44

MON

29

1918 - Fleet mutiny
against war, Germany

TUE

30

1993 - Loyalists
shoot 7 dead in
village pub,
Greysteel, Northern
Ireland

WED   ◑

31

1937 - Death of
Dick Sheppard,
founder of PPU,
London, Britain

1

1888 - Fenner
Brockway, peace
parliamentarian,
born, India

2

1920 - Gaoled anti-
war activist Eugene
Debs receives 1
million votes as
Presidential
candidate, USA

3

1918 - Armistice
between Austria and
Allies signed

4

1918 - Allied
Conference agrees
peace terms for
offer to Germany,
Versailles, France

On behalf of 71% of Spaniards, I respectfully request General Franco, Saviour of his country, to call free elections for the office of Head of State.

Poster, enacting his novel, *Los Encartelados, The Poster People*, for which Gonzalo Arias was arrested, 20 October 1968

WEEK 45

MON

5

1978 - Voters agree
to leave nuclear
reactor unfuelled,
Zwentendorf, Austria

TUE

6

1918 - German
armistice
commission meets
Allied delegation,
Compiègne, France

WED

●

7

1978 - Voters ban
nuclear power,
Missoula, Montana,
USA

THU

8

1992 - 350,000
protest against racist
violence, Berlin,
Germany

FRI

9

1938 - *Kristallnacht*,
night of deepening
repression of Jews,
Germany

WORLD SCIENCE DAY FOR
PEACE & DEVELOPMENT

SAT

10

1998 - UN votes for
Decade for a
Culture of Peace &
Nonviolence for the
Children of the
World

MARTINMAS
REMEMBRANCE DAY (UK/CAN)

SUN

11

1918 - Armistice
ending WWI signed,
Compiègne, France

November

It has been a woman's task throughout history to go on believing in life when there was almost no hope. If we are united, we may be able to produce a world in which our children and other people's children can be safe.

Margaret Mead

VETERANS' DAY OBSERVED (US)
(HOL CAN/US)

MON

12

1987 - 5 WRI members arrested for attempting personal peace treaties, Wroclaw, Poland

TUE

13

1918 - Treaty of Brest-Litovsk, with Germany, annulled by Soviet government

WED

14

1998 - 160 states set timetable for dealing with global warming

THU
15
1978 - Death of
Margaret Mead,
exponent of war as
only an invention,
USA

FRI
16
1968 - 5000 defy ban
in marching for civil
rights, Londonderry,
N Ireland

SAT
17
1858 - Death of
Robert Owen, co-
operative venturer,
Newtown, Wales

SUN
18
1978 - Farmers
plough site of
proposed nuclear
power station,
Torness, Scotland

November

Society may be formed so as to exist without crime, without poverty, with health greatly improved, with little, if any, misery, and with intelligence and happiness increased a hundredfold; and no obstacle whatsoever intervenes at this moment, except ignorance, to prevent such a state of society becoming universal.

Robert Owen, *An Address for Better Working Conditions in England*, 1816

WEEK 47

MON
19

1998 - First stage troop withdrawal from West Bank approved by Israel

TUE
20

UNIVERSAL CHILDREN'S DAY

1987 - SANE and FREEZE merge, USA

WED
21

1998 - 7000 protest against School of the Americas, Fort Benning, Georgia, USA

THANKSGIVING (HOL US)

THU

22

1998 - 2370 risk
arrest by "crossing
the line" at School of
the Americas
protest, Fort Bening,
Georgia, USA

○

FRI

23

1992 - After 6-year
boycott by INFACT,
GE sells Aerospace
Division making
nuclear weapons,
USA

SAT

24

1992 - US military
presence ends,
Philippines

INT'L DAY FOR ELIMINATION OF
VIOLENCE AGAINST WOMEN

SUN

25

1987 - Charter '87
for Refugees
launched,
Westminster Abbey,
London, Britain

November~December

No one has a right to sit down and feel hopeless. There's too much work to do.

Dorothy Day

MON

26

1968 - UN
Resolution against
Capital Punishment

TUE

27

1988 - Graffiti
painted on fighter
planes due for
Turkey, Woensdrecht
airbase, Netherlands

WED

28

1990 -
Demonstration in
support of CO
Ronald Jean Baptiste,
McGuire USAF base,
New Jersey, USA

THU
29
1990 - UN Security
Council votes 12-2
for war in Gulf

FRI
30
1980 - Death of
Dorothy Day, co-
founder of Catholic
Worker movement,
USA

PRISONERS FOR PEACE DAY

SAT
1
1948 - Abolition of
army comes into
effect, Costa Rica

ADVENT SUNDAY

SUN
2
1983 - Convention
prohibiting inhumane
weapons comes into
force

December

I pledge allegiance to the world,
To cherish every living thing,
To care for earth and sea and air,
With peace and freedom everywhere.

Lillian Genser, Women's International League for Peace and Freedom

WEEK 49

MON

3

1992 - International Day of Disabled Persons first observed

TUE

4

1968 - 264 arrested in protest at military induction centre, New York, USA

WED

5

1987 - International Volunteer Day for Economic and Social Development first observed

THU

6

1958 - 46 enter Thor rocket site to prevent construction, North Pickenham, Norfolk, Britain

FRI

7

1988 - President Mikhail Gorbachev announces to UN unilateral reduction of armed forces by 500,000, USSR

SAT

8

1988 - 12 arrested for hammering on cruise missile bunkers, Woensdrecht, Netherlands

SUN

9

1981 - Mike Cooley awarded "alternative Nobel Peace Prize" for arms conversion, Stockholm, Sweden

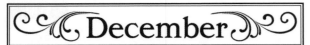

December

*If nations could overcome the mutual fear and mistrust whose
sombre shadow is now thrown over the world, and could meet
with confidence and goodwill to settle their possible differences,
they would easily be able to establish a lasting peace.*

Fridtjof Nansen

MON

10

1938 - Nansen
International Office
for Refugees
awarded Nobel
Peace Prize, Oslo,
Norway

TUE

11

1992 - 160 states
agree to end world
hunger, Rome, Italy

WED

12

1958 - Maurice
McCrackin gaoled 6
months for war tax
resistance, USA

THU

13

1887 - John
McGovern,
parliamentary
antimilitarist, born,
Scotland

FRI

14

1991 - 20,000 march
for end to civil war,
El Salvador

SAT

15

1978 - Building of
nuclear reactor
prohibited, Austria

SUN

16

1981 - In response
to massive protests,
test drilling
suspended at 20
potential nuclear
waste sites, Britain

December

Survivors of thermonuclear war, if such there are, will envy the dead.

Norman Thomas, *The Prerequisites of Peace*

MON

17

1998 - British/US
airstrikes renewed
against Iraq

TUE

18

1969 - Death penalty
for murder finally
abolished, Britain

WED

19

1968 - Death of
Norman Thomas,
socialist pacifist, USA

20

1978 - UN General Assembly recognises conscientious objection to enforcement of apartheid

SOLSTICE

21

1991 - Authorities publish list of draft resisters and deserters, Kragujevac, Serbia, Yugoslavia

○

22

1943 - Racial segregation ends after 4-month strike by 23 COs, Federal Penitentiary, Danbury, Connecticut, USA

23

1991 - Prayers for peace in all churches, but peace rally banned, Belgrade, Serbia, Yugoslavia

December

Our sole safeguard against the very real danger of a reversion to barbarism is the kind of morality which compels the individual conscience, be the group right or wrong. The individual conscience against the atom bomb? Yes. There is no other way.

Life Magazine, USA, 20 August 1945

WEEK 52

MON

24

1991 - Parents of reservists from Grocka protest at Army HQ, Belgrade, Serbia, Yugoslavia

TUE

25

CHRISTMAS DAY
(HOL UK/IRE/CAN/US)

1978 - Vietnamese troops invade Cambodia

WED

26

ST STEPHEN'S DAY
(HOL UK/IRE/CAN)

1988 - Funeral of Chico Mendes, murdered for his struggle against destruction of rain forests, Brazil

27

1993 - 12 killed over
2 days of Bosnian
Serb shelling,
Sarajevo, Bosnia

HOLY INNOCENTS' DAY

28

1968 -
Anti-conscription
conference launches
"Don't Register"
campaign, Australia

29

1958 - First meeting
of Economic
Commission for
Africa

30

1964 - UNCTAD
established

December ∽ January

Although the world is very full of suffering, it is also full of the overcoming of it.
Helen Keller

MON

31

NEW YEAR'S EVE

1981 - Military coup
d'état, Ghana

TUE

1

NEW YEAR'S DAY
(HOL UK/IRE/CAN/US)
WORLD PEACE DAY

2019 - Suggested
dates (and
quotations) for
future diaries
welcome anytime

WED

2

(HOL SCOT)

Forward Planner 2019

	January		February		March	
Mon						
Tue	1	1				
Wed	2					
Thu	3					
Fri	4		1		1	
Sat	5		2		2	
Sun	6		3		3	
Mon	7	2	4	6	4	10
Tue	8		5		5	
Wed	9		6		6	
Thu	10		7		7	
Fri	11		8		8	
Sat	12		9		9	
Sun	13		10		10	
Mon	14	3	11	7	11	11
Tue	15		12		12	
Wed	16		13		13	
Thu	17		14		14	
Fri	18		15		15	
Sat	19		16		16	
Sun	20		17		17	
Mon	21	4	18	8	18	12
Tue	22		19		19	
Wed	23		20		20	
Thu	24		21		21	
Fri	25		22		22	
Sat	26		23		23	
Sun	27		24		24	
Mon	28	5	25	9	25	13
Tue	29		26		26	
Wed	30		27		27	
Thu	31		28		28	
Fri					29	
Sat					30	
Sun					31	

Forward Planner 2019

	April		May		June	
Mon	1	14				
Tue	2					
Wed	3		1			
Thu	4		2			
Fri	5		3			
Sat	6		4		1	
Sun	7		5		2	
Mon	8	15	6	19	3	23
Tue	9		7		4	
Wed	10		8		5	
Thu	11		9		6	
Fri	12		10		7	
Sat	13		11		8	
Sun	14		12		9	
Mon	15	16	13	20	10	24
Tue	16		14		11	
Wed	17		15		12	
Thu	18		16		13	
Fri	19		17		14	
Sat	20		18		15	
Sun	21		19		16	
Mon	22	17	20	21	17	25
Tue	23		21		18	
Wed	24		22		19	
Thu	25		23		20	
Fri	26		24		21	
Sat	27		25		22	
Sun	28		26		23	
Mon	29	18	27	22	24	26
Tue	30		28		25	
Wed			29		26	
Thu			30		27	
Fri			31		28	
Sat					29	
Sun					30	

Forward Planner 2019

	July		August		September	
Mon	1	27				
Tue	2					
Wed	3					
Thu	4		1			
Fri	5		2			
Sat	6		3			
Sun	7		4		1	
Mon	8	28	5	32	2	36
Tue	9		6		3	
Wed	10		7		4	
Thu	11		8		5	
Fri	12		9		6	
Sat	13		10		7	
Sun	14		11		8	
Mon	15	29	12	33	9	37
Tue	16		13		10	
Wed	17		14		11	
Thu	18		15		12	
Fri	19		16		13	
Sat	20		17		14	
Sun	21		18		15	
Mon	22	30	19	34	16	38
Tue	23		20		17	
Wed	24		21		18	
Thu	25		22		19	
Fri	26		23		20	
Sat	27		24		21	
Sun	28		25		22	
Mon	29	31	26	35	23	39
Tue	30		27		24	
Wed	31		28		25	
Thu			29		26	
Fri			30		27	
Sat			31		28	
Sun					29	
Mon					30	40

Forward Planner 2019

	October		November		December	
Mon						
Tue	1					
Wed	2					
Thu	3					
Fri	4		1			
Sat	5		2			
Sun	6		3		1	
Mon	7	41	4	45	2	49
Tue	8		5		3	
Wed	9		6		4	
Thu	10		7		5	
Fri	11		8		6	
Sat	12		9		7	
Sun	13		10		8	
Mon	14	42	11	46	9	50
Tue	15		12		10	
Wed	16		13		11	
Thu	17		14		12	
Fri	18		15		13	
Sat	19		16		14	
Sun	20		17		15	
Mon	21	43	18	47	16	51
Tue	22		19		17	
Wed	23		20		18	
Thu	24		21		19	
Fri	25		22		20	
Sat	26		23		21	
Sun	27		24		22	
Mon	28	44	25	48	23	52
Tue	29		26		24	
Wed	30		27		25	
Thu	31		28		26	
Fri			29		27	
Sat			30		28	
Sun					29	
Mon					30	1
Tue					31	

Calendar 2017

JANUARY

MON	2	9	16	23	30
TUE	3	10	17	24	31
WED	4	11	18	25	
THU	5	12	19	26	
FRI	6	13	20	27	
SAT	7	14	21	28	
SUN	1	8	15	22	29

FEBRUARY

MON	6	13	20	27
TUE	7	14	21	28
WED	1	8	15	22
THU	2	9	16	23
FRI	3	10	17	24
SAT	4	11	18	25
SUN	5	12	19	26

MARCH

MON	6	13	20	27	
TUE	7	14	21	28	
WED	1	8	15	22	29
THU	2	9	16	23	30
FRI	3	10	17	24	31
SAT	4	11	18	25	
SUN	5	12	19	26	

APRIL

MON	3	10	17	24
TUE	4	11	18	25
WED	5	12	19	26
THU	6	13	20	27
FRI	7	14	21	28
SAT	1	8	15	22	29
SUN	2	9	16	23	30

MAY

MON	1	8	15	22	29
TUE	2	9	16	23	30
WED	3	10	17	24	31
THU	4	11	18	25	
FRI	5	12	19	26	
SAT	6	13	20	27	
SUN	7	14	21	28	

JUNE

MON	5	12	19	26	
TUE	6	13	20	27	
WED	7	14	21	28	
THU	1	8	15	22	29
FRI	2	9	16	23	30
SAT	3	10	17	24	
SUN	4	11	18	25	

JULY

MON	3	10	17	24	31
TUE	4	11	18	25	
WED	5	12	19	26	
THU	6	13	20	27	
FRI	7	14	21	28	
SAT	1	8	15	22	29
SUN	2	9	16	23	30

AUGUST

MON	7	14	21	28	
TUE	1	8	15	22	29
WED	2	9	16	23	30
THU	3	10	17	24	31
FRI	4	11	18	25	
SAT	5	12	19	26	
SUN	6	13	20	27	

SEPTEMBER

MON	4	11	18	25
TUE	5	12	19	26
WED	6	13	20	27
THU	7	14	21	28
FRI	1	8	15	22	29
SAT	2	9	16	23	30
SUN	3	10	17	24

OCTOBER

MON	2	9	16	23	30
TUE	3	10	17	24	31
WED	4	11	18	25	
THU	5	12	19	26	
FRI	6	13	20	27	
SAT	7	14	21	28	
SUN	1	8	15	22	29

NOVEMBER

MON	6	13	20	27	
TUE	7	14	21	28	
WED	1	8	15	22	29
THU	2	9	16	23	30
FRI	3	10	17	24	
SAT	4	11	18	25	
SUN	5	12	19	26	

DECEMBER

MON	4	11	18	25	
TUE	5	12	19	26	
WED	6	13	20	27	
THU	7	14	21	28	
FRI	1	8	15	22	29
SAT	2	9	16	23	30
SUN	3	10	17	24	31

Calendar 2018

JANUARY

MON	1 8 15 22 29
TUE	2 9 16 23 30
WED	3 10 17 24 31
THU	4 11 18 25
FRI	5 12 19 26
SAT	6 13 20 27
SUN	7 14 21 28

FEBRUARY

MON	5 12 19 26
TUE	6 13 20 27
WED	7 14 21 28
THU	1 8 15 22
FRI	2 9 16 23
SAT	3 10 17 24
SUN	4 11 18 25

MARCH

MON	5 12 19 26
TUE	6 13 20 27
WED	7 14 21 28
THU	1 8 15 22 29
FRI	2 9 16 23 30
SAT	3 10 17 24 31
SUN	4 11 18 25

APRIL

MON	2 9 16 23 30
TUE	3 10 17 24
WED	4 11 18 25
THU	5 12 19 26
FRI	6 13 20 27
SAT	7 14 21 28
SUN	1 8 15 22 29

MAY

MON	7 14 21 28
TUE	1 8 15 22 29
WED	2 9 16 23 30
THU	3 10 17 24 31
FRI	4 11 18 25
SAT	5 12 19 26
SUN	6 13 20 27

JUNE

MON	4 11 18 25
TUE	5 12 19 26
WED	6 13 20 27
THU	7 14 21 28
FRI	1 8 15 22 29
SAT	2 9 16 23 30
SUN	3 10 17 24

JULY

MON	2 9 16 23 30
TUE	3 10 17 24 31
WED	4 11 18 25
THU	5 12 19 26
FRI	6 13 20 27
SAT	7 14 21 28
SUN	1 8 15 22 29

AUGUST

MON	6 13 20 27
TUE	7 14 21 28
WED	1 8 15 22 29
THU	2 9 16 23 30
FRI	3 10 17 24 31
SAT	4 11 18 25
SUN	5 12 19 26

SEPTEMBER

MON	3 10 17 24
TUE	4 11 18 25
WED	5 12 19 26
THU	6 13 20 27
FRI	7 14 21 28
SAT	1 8 15 22 29
SUN	2 9 16 23 30

OCTOBER

MON	1 8 15 22 29
TUE	2 9 16 23 30
WED	3 10 17 24 31
THU	4 11 18 25
FRI	5 12 19 26
SAT	6 13 20 27
SUN	7 14 21 28

NOVEMBER

MON	5 12 19 26
TUE	6 13 20 27
WED	7 14 21 28
THU	1 8 15 22 29
FRI	2 9 16 23 30
SAT	3 10 17 24
SUN	4 11 18 25

DECEMBER

MON	3 10 17 24 31
TUE	4 11 18 25
WED	5 12 19 26
THU	6 13 20 27
FRI	7 14 21 28
SAT	1 8 15 22 29
SUN	2 9 16 23 30

Calendar 2019

JANUARY

MON	7 14 21 28
TUE	1 8 15 22 29
WED	2 9 16 23 30
THU	3 10 17 24 31
FRI	4 11 18 25
SAT	5 12 19 26
SUN	6 13 20 27

FEBRUARY

MON	4 11 18 25
TUE	5 12 19 26
WED	6 13 20 27
THU	7 14 21 28
FRI	1 8 15 22
SAT	2 9 16 23
SUN	3 10 17 24

MARCH

MON	4 11 18 25
TUE	5 12 19 26
WED	6 13 20 27
THU	7 14 21 28
FRI	1 8 15 22 29
SAT	2 9 16 23 30
SUN	3 10 17 24 31

APRIL

MON	1 8 15 22 29
TUE	2 9 16 23 30
WED	3 10 17 24
THU	4 11 18 25
FRI	5 12 19 26
SAT	6 13 20 27
SUN	7 14 21 28

MAY

MON	6 13 20 27
TUE	7 14 21 28
WED	1 8 15 22 29
THU	2 9 16 23 30
FRI	3 10 17 24 31
SAT	4 11 18 25
SUN	5 12 19 26

JUNE

MON	3 10 17 24
TUE	4 11 18 25
WED	5 12 19 26
THU	6 13 20 27
FRI	7 14 21 28
SAT	1 8 15 22 29
SUN	2 9 16 23 30

JULY

MON	1 8 15 22 29
TUE	2 9 16 23 30
WED	3 10 17 24 31
THU	4 11 18 25
FRI	5 12 19 26
SAT	6 13 20 27
SUN	7 14 21 28

AUGUST

MON	5 12 19 26
TUE	6 13 20 27
WED	7 14 21 28
THU	1 8 15 22 29
FRI	2 9 16 23 30
SAT	3 10 17 24 31
SUN	4 11 18 25

SEPTEMBER

MON	2 9 16 23 30
TUE	3 10 17 24
WED	4 11 18 25
THU	5 12 19 26
FRI	6 13 20 27
SAT	7 14 21 28
SUN	1 8 15 22 29

OCTOBER

MON	7 14 21 28
TUE	1 8 15 22 29
WED	2 9 16 23 30
THU	3 10 17 24 31
FRI	4 11 18 25
SAT	5 12 19 26
SUN	6 13 20 27

NOVEMBER

MON	4 11 18 25
TUE	5 12 19 26
WED	6 13 20 27
THU	7 14 21 28
FRI	1 8 15 22 29
SAT	2 9 16 23 30
SUN	3 10 17 24

DECEMBER

MON	2 9 16 23 30
TUE	3 10 17 24 31
WED	4 11 18 25
THU	5 12 19 26
FRI	6 13 20 27
SAT	7 14 21 28
SUN	1 8 15 22 29

HOUSMANS
World Peace Directory
● 2018 ●

This comprehensive and up-to-date Directory is provided for the *Peace Diary* by the **Housmans Peace Resource Project**, and edited by Albert Beale. **To make the best use of it, please read the next two pages.**

There is a difficult balance to be struck between the usefulness, for many people, of the information in this format, and the fact that the full World Peace Database — from which this Directory is derived — is available on-line at **www.housmans.info/wpd**. Your feedback about this is encouraged.

Groups omitted from this printed version tend to be the more localised or specialised groups — and those which are least efficient at responding to communications from the database editor! The complete on-line information is searchable, and it is also possible to obtain your own copy of the full database.

To keep the database up to date, organisations are contacted regularly by post, and also (where possible) by e-mail. But we rely on other input as well: if your group changes any of its contact details, please send the information without waiting to be asked. There is never a wrong time to send information.

Some information, such as changes in telephone numbering systems, is often available in the country concerned long before it can be obtained elsewhere — so please help by sending any such information you know of.

All correspondence about the Directory should be sent to: **Housmans Peace Resource Project, 5 Caledonian Road, London N1, UK (tel +44-20-7278 4474; fax +44-20-7278 0444; e-mail worldpeace@gn.apc.org)**. Information is preferred in writing.

Directory Introduction

This is the 65th Peace Directory to be published with the Housmans Peace Diary. It is intended to help people find contact points for issues which interest them, and also to be a day-to-day reference resource for activists.

What's in the Directory?

The 2018 Directory lists over 1400 national and international organisations, covering the breadth of the peace movement – with the emphasis on grassroots, non-governmental groups – as well as major bodies in related fields such as environmental and human rights campaigning.

This year, around one-third of the groups listed have either had their information amended since last year's Directory, or are newly included this year.

How to find things in the Directory

Check both the national and international listings if necessary. If you can't find exactly what you want, try a less specialised organisation which might include what you're looking for. (And see the previous page for the availability of further information.)

International organisations are listed alphabetically. The national listings are in alphabetical order of English-language country name; the organisations are then arranged alphabetically within each country. Organisations' names (and addresses) are generally in the language of the country concerned.

Whilst aware of political sensitivities, we use commonly accepted postal and administrative divisions of the world to decide what is or isn't a "country". This doesn't mean we support or oppose countries' divisions or mergers – we just want the Directory to be easy to use.

In the national listings we don't repeat the country name at the end of each address, so you will need to add it.

How the entries are set out

The organisation's name is in **bold print**; or, if the name is that of a magazine, in ***bold italics***. Any common abbreviation is shown [in square brackets], in **bold** or ***bold italics*** as appropriate. Most organisations then have codes (in round brackets) giving an indication of their politics and activities (**see Note 1**). The address is shown next. Then we give (in brackets) any telephone number (**see Note 2**), fax number (**see Note 3**), electronic mail address (**see Note 4**), and web site address (**see Note 4**). Magazines published by the organisation are then shown in *italics*. Where the listing is itself a publication, details of frequency etc may be given next (**see Note 5**). There may be brief additional information where necessary.

The **Notes**, including our standard abbreviations, are given opposite.

Notes

1. Codes used to explain something about the listed organisation are as follows. The codes for international bodies in the left-hand column are used to show an official link to tbe body (or to one of its national affiliates in the country concerned). If these are not sufficient, the general codes on the right are used.

AI Amnesty International	**AL** Alternativist / Anarchist
FE Friends of the Earth International	**AT** Arms Trade / Conversion
FR International Fellowship of Reconciliation	**CD** Citizen Diplomacy / People-to-People
GP Greenpeace International	**CR** Conflict Resolution / Mediation
IB International Peace Bureau	**DA** Disarmament / Arms Control
IP International Physicians for the Prevention of Nuclear War	**EL** Environmental / Ecological
	HR Equality / Minority & Human Rights
	ND Nuclear Disarmament
PC Pax Christi International	**PA** Anti-Militarist / Pacifist
SC Service Civil International	**PO** Positive Action / Lifestyle
SE Servas International	**RA** Radical Action / Direct Action
SF Society of Friends (Quakers)	**RE** Research into Peace, Conflict / Peace Education
UN World Federation of United Nations Associations	**RP** Religious Peace Group
	SD Social Defence / Civilian-Based Defence
WL Women's International League for Peace and Freedom	**TR** War Tax Resistance / Peace Tax Campaigning
WP World Peace Council	**TW** Development / Liberation / Third World
WR War Resisters' International	**WC** International Workcamps
	WF World Federalists / World Citizens

2. Telephone numbers are given in standard international format: +[country code]-[area code]-[local number]. The "+" indicates the international access code used in the country you're phoning from. The area code (if there is one) is given without any national trunk prefix digit(s) that are used in the country concerned – for calls *within* the country you must add them if they exist. Exceptionally, a few countries without area codes still require an extra digit (generally 0) at the start of their national number for internal calls; the main culprits are Belgium, France, Switzerland, South Africa and Thailand. Note that for calls between neighbouring countries there are often non-standard codes outside the normal system.

3. The telephone number of a facsimile (telefax) machine is given without repeating codes which are the same as in the preceding ordinary telephone number; "fax" alone means the fax number is identical to the phone number. Because many groups share a fax machine, always start your message by saying clearly which person and organisation it is meant for.

4. The e-mail and web site addresses are given in standard internet format. (The e-mail address is the one with the "@" in it.) The "http://" which, by definition, starts every web address is **not** repeated each time here.

5. Abbreviations used in connection with publications are:

dly daily	**x yrly** x per year	**ea** each
wkly weekly	**annl** annual	**pa** per annum
ftly fortnightly	**irreg** irregular	**ftm** free to members
mthly monthly	**occl** occasional	**nfp** no fixed price / donation

INTERNATIONAL ORGANISATIONS

Abolition 2000 International Secretariat (ND EL), c/o Western States Legal Foundation, 655 13th St - Suite 201, Preservation Park, Oakland, CA 94612, USA (+1-510-839 5877) (wslf@earthlink.net) (www.abolition2000.org). Network to achieve nuclear weapons abolition convention.

Alliance Against Genocide (HR), c/o Genocide Watch, 3351 N Fairfax Dr - MS4D3, Arlington, VA 22201, USA (+1-202-643 1405) (communications@genocidewatch.org) (www.againstgenocide.org). Formerly International Alliance to End Genocide.

Alternatives to Violence Project International (CR), PO Box 164, Purchase, NY 10577, USA (avp.international). International network of national AVP organisations. AVP groups organise training to aid creative responses to potentially violent situations.

Amnesty International - International Secretariat (HR RE), Peter Benenson House, 1 Easton St, London WC1X 0DW, Britain (+44-20-7413 5500) (fax 7956 1157) (contactus@amnesty.org) (www.amnesty.org). *Newsletter; Annual Report.* EU office +32-2 502 1499; East Asia office (Hong Kong) +852-3963 7197; Southern Africa office (Johannesburg) +27-11-283 6000; Middle East and North Africa office (Beirut) +961-1-748751.

Architects & Planners for Justice in Palestine [APJP] (HR), 100 Whitchurch Lane, Edgware, Middx HA8 6QN, Britain (info@apjp.org) (apjp.org).

ARTICLE 19 - Global Campaign for Free Expression (HR), Free Word Centre, 60 Farringdon Rd, London EC1, Britain (+44-20-7324 2500) (info@article19.org) (www.article19.org). Also in Brazil (+55-11-3057 0042) (brasil@article19.org); in Mexico (+52-55-1054 6500) (mexico@article19.org); in East Africa (+254-20-386 2230) (africa@article19.org).

Asian Human Rights Commission [AHRC] (HR), Unit 1 & 2 - 12/F, Hopeful Factory Centre, 10-16 Wo Shing St, Fotan, NT, Hong Kong (+852-2698 6339) (fax 2698 6367) (communications@ahrc.asia) (www.humanrights.asia). Engage in daily interventions as well as institutional issues.

Association of World Citizens [AWC] (WF CD RE), PO Box 1206, Novato, CA 94948-1206, USA (+1-415-893 1369) (suezipp@worldcitizen.org) (www.worldcitizensunited.org).

Association pour la Prévention de la Torture / Association for the Prevention of Torture [APT] (HR), BP 137, 1211 Genève 19, Switzerland (+41-22 919 2170) (fax 22 919 2180) (apt@apt.ch) (www.apt.ch). Works to improve legal frameworks and detention monitoring, to prevent torture and other ill-treatment.

Bahá'í International Community - Office of Public Information (RP), PO Box 155, 3100101 Haifa, Israel (+972-4-835 8194) (fax 835 3312) (opi@bwc.org) (www.bahai.org). *One Country.* Magazine office: Suite 120, 866 UN Plaza, New York, NY 10017, USA.

Bellona Foundation (EL), Vulkan 11, 0178 Oslo, Norway (+47-2323 4600) (fax 2238 3862) (info@bellona.no) (bellona.org). Other international office in Brussels. Offices also in Russia (Murmansk and St Petersburg).

Campaign to Stop Killer Robots (DA HR), c/o Human Rights Watch Washington Office, 1630 Connecticut Ave NW - Suite 500, Washington, DC 20009, USA (+1-202-612 4360) (wareham@hrw.org) (www.stopkillerrobots.org). Work to pre-emptively ban fully autonomous weapons. Network of national and international peace and human rights organisations.

Carta de la Paz / Letter of Peace (RE), C/Modolell 41, 08021 Barcelona, Spain (+34-93 414 5936) (fax) (secretaria@cartadelapaz.org) (www.letterofpeace.org). *Information Paper.* Petition to UN. South America office, Chile: +56-2-274 7151. Central America and Caribbean, Dominican Republic: +1809-508 6879. North America, Mexico: +52-66-2213 9827. Central Europe, Switzerland: +41-22-860 2304.

Center for Global Nonkilling [CGNK] (RE PA), 3653 Tantalus Dr, Honolulu, HI 96822-5033, USA (+1-808-536 7442) (info@nonkilling.org) (nonkilling.org). To promote change towards the measurable goal of a killing-free world.

Child Soldiers International (RE PA AT), 4th Floor, 9 Marshalsea Rd, Borough, London SE1 1EP, Britain (+44-20-7367 4110) (fax 7367 4129) (info@child-soldiers.org) (www.child-soldiers.org).

Church and Peace (SF FR PC), Ringstr 14, 35641 Schoeffengrund, Germany (+49-6445-5588) (fax 5070) (IntlOffice@church-and-peace.org) (www.church-and-peace.org). *Theology and Peace / Théologie et Paix / Theologie und Frieden.* European ecumenical network.

Co-ordinating Committee for International Voluntary Service [CCIVS] (SC TW WC EL HR), UNESCO House, 1 rue Miollis, 75732 Paris Cedex 15, France (+33-14568 4936) (fax 14568 4934) (secretariat@ccivs.org) (www.ccivs.org).

Coalition for the International Criminal Court - UN Office [CICC] (HR), WFM, 708 Third Ave - Suite 1715, New York, NY 10017, USA (+1-212-687 2863) (fax 599 1332) (cicc@coalitionfortheicc.org) (www.coalitionfortheicc.org). Also ICC office, Den Haag (+31-70-311 1080) (cicc-hague@coalitionfortheicc.org).

INTERNATIONAL ORGANISATIONS

Coalition Mondiale Contre la Peine de Mort / World Coalition Against the Death Penalty (HR), 69 rue Michelet, 93100 Montreuil, France (+33-18089 4505) (fax 14870 2225) (contact@worldcoalition.org) (www.worldcoalition.org).

Community of Christ - Peace and Justice Ministries International Office (RP CR TW), 1001 W Walnut, Independence, MO 64050-3562, USA (+1-816-833 1000) (fax 521 3082) (shalom@CofChrist.org) (www.CofChrist.org/peacejustice).

Conscience and Peace Tax International [CPTI] (TR), c/o Conscience, 17 North Square, London NW11, Britain (+44-20-3515 9132) (co.sec@cpti.co) (www.cpti.ws). *CPTI Bulletin.*

Coordination Internationale pour une Culture de Non-violence et de Paix (RE PO DA), 148 rue du Faubourg Saint Denis, 75010 Paris, France (+33-14036 0660) (secretariat@nvpnetwork.net) (www.nvpnetwork.net). International Network for a Culture of Nonviolence and Peace.

Corporate Europe Observatory [CEO] (EL HR TW), Rue d'Édimbourg 18-26, 1050 Bruxelles, Belgium (+32-2 893 0930) (ceo@corporateeurope.org) (www.corporateeurope.org). Targets threats to democracy, justice and the environment posed by corporations.

EarthAction International (IB EL TW AT CR), PO Box 63, Amherst, MA 01004, USA (+1-413-549 8118) (fax 256 8871) (contact@earthaction.org) (www.earthaction.org). *EarthAction Alerts.* Chile office (+56-2-732 5976) (e-mail contacto@accionporlatierra.cl).

Ecumenical Accompaniment Programme in Palestine and Israel [EAPPI] (RP HR CD CR SF), c/o World Council of Churches (Public Witness section), PO Box 2100, 1211 Genève 2, Switzerland (+41-22 791 6108) (fax 22 791 6122) (eappi@wcc-coe.org) (www.eappi.org). Accompanying Palestinians and Israelis in non-violent actions; advocacy to end occupation. Also: PO Box 741, Jerusalem 91000 (+972-2-626 2458).

Eirene - Internationaler Christlicher Friedensdienst / International Christian Service for Peace (FR TW CR), Postfach 1322, 56503 Neuwied, Germany (+49-2631-83790) (fax 837990) (eirene-int@eirene.org) (www.eirene.org). Affiliated groups in Netherlands, Switzerland. German group now combined with international office.

European Bureau for Conscientious Objection [EBCO] (WR SC), 35 Rue Van Elewyck, 1050 Bruxelles, Belgium (+32-2 648 5220) (ebco@ebco-beoc.org) (www.ebco-beoc.org).

European Initiative Against TTIP and CETA (EL HR), Marienstr 19/20, 10117 Berlin, Germany (+49-30-2848 2379) (info@stop-ttip.org) (stop-ttip.org). Campaign against plans for trade deals which give corporations power over democratic institutions.

European Network Against Arms Trade [ENAAT] (AT), Anna Spenglerstr 71, 1054 NH Amsterdam, Netherlands (+31-20-616 4684) (info@stopwapenhandel.org) (www.enaat.org).

European Network for Civil Peace Services [EN.CPS] (CR CD PA HR), c/o Helga Tempel, Foehrenstieg 8, 22926 Ahrensburg, Germany (+49-4102-53337) (helga.tempel@gmx.de) (www.en-cps.org).

European Network for Peace and Human Rights (AT ND RE), c/o Bertrand Russell Peace Foundation, Russell House, Bulwell La, Nottingham NG6, Britain (+44-115-978 4504) (fax 942 0433) (elfeuro@compuserve.com) (www.russfound.org). *The Spokesman.*

Every Casualty (RE), c/o Oxford Research Group, Development House, 56-64 Leonard St, London EC2, Britain (+44-20-7549 0298) (team@everycasualty.org) (www.everycasualty.org). Systematic documentation of conflict casualties. Aims to ensure that the full cost of conflict is known and can be understood.

Fédération Internationale de l'Action des Chrétiens pour l'Abolition de la Torture [FIACAT] (HR), 27 rue de Maubeuge, 75009 Paris, France (+33-14280 0160) (fax 14280 2089) (fiacat@fiacat.org) (www.fiacat.org).

Foundation for the International Prevention of Genocide and Mass Atrocities (HR), Villányi út 47, 1118 Budapest, Hungary (+36-21-252 4525) (fax) (info@budapestcentre.eu) (www.genocideprevention.eu).

Friends of the Earth International [FoEI] (EL), PO Box 19199, 1000 GD Amsterdam, Netherlands (+31-20-622 1369) (fax 639 2181) (www.foei.org). Europe office: Mundo-B Building, Rue d'Edimbourg 26, 1050 Bruxelles, Belgium (+32-2 893 1000) (fax 2 893 1035) (info@foeeurope.org) (www.foeeurope.org).

Friends World Committee for Consultation [FWCC] (SF), 173 Euston Rd, London NW1, Britain (+44-20-7663 1199) (world@friendsworldoffice.org) (fwccworld.org). Also 4 regional offices. Africa: PO Box 41946, Nairobi, Kenya; Americas: 1506 Race St, Philadelphia, PA 19102, USA; Asia & West Pacific: PO Box 6063, O'Connor, ACT 2602, Australia; Europe & Middle East: PO Box 1157, Histon CB24 9XQ, Cambs, Britain.

INTERNATIONAL ORGANISATIONS

Geneva Centre for the Democratic Control of Armed Forces [DCAF] (CR HR RE), PO Box 1360, 1211 Genève 1, Switzerland (+41-22 741 7700) (fax 22 741 7705) (info@dcaf.ch) (www.dcaf.ch). EU office in Brussels. Offices also in Lebanon, Palestine, Slovenia, Tunisia.

Gesellschaft für Bedrohte Völker - International (HR TW), Postfach 2024, 37010 Göttingen, Germany (+49-551-499060) (fax 58028) (info@gfbv.de) (www.gfbv.de). *Pogrom.* Society for Threatened Peoples. Campaigns against genocide and ethnocide.

Global Action to Prevent War (RE ND DA HR), 866 UN Plaza - Suite 4050, New York, NY 10017, USA (+1-212-818 1815) (fax 818 1857) (coordinator@globalactionpw.org) (www.globalactionpw.org). Transnational civil society and academic network. Legacy of World Order Models Project in 1990s. Aims for "integrated approach to enhancing security and ending war-related violence".

Global Anabaptist Peace Commission (RP), c/o Mennonite World Conference, 50 Kent Ave - Suite 206, Kitchener, ON, N2G 3R1, Canada (+1-519-571 0060) (fax 226-647 4224) (Kitchener@mwc-cmm.org) (www.mwc-cmm.org/article/about-peace-commission). Previously Global Anabaptist Peace and Justice Network.

Global Campaign on Military Spending - Coordination Office [GCOMS] (DA AT), c/o Centre Delàs d'Estudis per la Pau, c/ Erasme de Janer 8 - entresol - despatx 9, 08001 Barcelona, Spain (coordination.gcoms@ipb.org) (demilitarize.org). Organise Global Day of Action on Military Spending. A project of the International Peace Bureau.

Global Ecumenical Network for the Abolition of Military Chaplaincies (RP), c/o IDK, Postfach 280312, 13443 Berlin, Germany (global-network@militaerseelsorge-abschaffen.de) (www.globnetabolishmilitarychaplaincy.webnode.com). Opposes co-option of churches by military, financial links between arms industry and churches, and churches' acceptance of warfare.

Global Initiative to End All Corporal Punishment of Children (HR), c/o APPROACH, Unit W (West) 125 Westminster Business Sq, 1-45 Durham St, London SE11, Britain (info@endcorporalpunishment.org) (www.endcorporalpunishment.org).

Global Partnership for the Prevention of Armed Conflict [GPPAC] (RE CR), Laan van Meerdervoort 70, 2517 AN Den Haag, Netherlands (+31-70-311 0970) (info@gppac.net) (www.gppac.net).

Global Policy Forum [GPF] (RE DA HR), 866 United Nations Plaza - Ste 4050, New York, NY 10017, USA (+1-646-553 3460) (gpf@globalpolicy.org) (www.globalpolicy.org). Policy watchdog monitoring work of United Nations. Mainly concerned with UN Security Council, food crisis, and economic issues. Promotes accountability and citizen participation in decision-making. Europe office in Bonn, Germany (europe@globalpolicy.org).

Green Cross International [GCI] (EL TW DA CR HR), 9-11 rue de Varembé, 1202 Genève, Switzerland (+41-22 789 1662) (fax 22 789 1695) (gcinternational@gci.ch) (www.gcint.org). Focuses on interface between security and sustainability, by working on conflicts arising from environmental degradation and on environmental consequences of warfare.

Greenpeace International (EL), Ottho Heldringstr 5, 1066 AZ Amsterdam, Netherlands (fax 718 2002) (info.int@greenpeace.org) (www.greenpeace.org/international).

Housmans Peace Resource Project [HPRP] (CD RE), 5 Caledonian Rd, London N1, Britain (+44-20-7278 4474) (fax 7278 0444) (worldpeace@gn.apc.org) (www.housmans.info). *Housmans World Peace Database & Directory.*

Human Rights Watch [HRW] (HR), Empire State Building - 34th Floor, 350 5th Ave, New York, NY 10118-3299, USA (+1-212-290 4700) (fax 736 1300) (www.hrw.org). EU liaison office in Brussels (+32-2 732 2009) (fax 2 732 0471). Offices also in: Britain, Canada, France, Germany, Japan, Netherlands, South Africa, Switzerland.

Human Rights Without Frontiers International [HRWF] (HR), Ave d'Auderghem 61, 1040 Bruxelles, Belgium (+32-2 345 6145) (international.secretariat.brussels@hrwf.net) (hrwf.net). Promotes culture of human rights in international organisations.

International Action Network on Small Arms [IANSA] (AT DA), c/o Action on Armed Violence, 2nd and 3rd Floor, 415 High Street, Stratford, London E15, Britain (communication@iansa.org) (www.iansa.org).

International Association of Lawyers Against Nuclear Arms [IALANA] (IB ND AT DA), Marienstr 19/20, 10117 Berlin, Germany (+49-30-2065 4857) (fax 2065 3837) (office@ialana.info) (www.ialana.info). UN office: c/o LCNP, +1-212-818 1861; Pacific office: +64-9-524 8403.

International Association of Lawyers Against Nuclear Arms - UN Office [IALANA] (IB ND AT DA), c/o LCNP, 866 UN Plaza - Suite 4050, New York, NY 10017-1936, USA (+1-212-818 1861) (fax 818 1857)

INTERNATIONAL ORGANISATIONS

(johnburroughs@lcnp.org) (www.ialana.info).
Main office, Germany (+49-30-2065 4857).
Pacific office (+64-9-524 8403).

International Campaign to Abolish Nuclear Weapons [ICAN] (ND), 150 Route de Ferney, 1211 Genève 2, Switzerland (+41-22 788 2063) (info@icanw.org) (www.icanw.org). Launched by IPPNW and others in 2007. Works towards a nuclear weapons convention. Asia Pacific office, Australia (+61-3-9023 1958).

International Campaign to Ban Landmines - Cluster Munitions Coalition [ICBL - CMC] (AT), 2 Chemin Eugène-Rigot, 1202 Genève, Switzerland (+41-22 920 0325) (fax 22 920 0115) (icbl@icbl.org) (www.icblcmc.org). Also www.icbl.org, www.stopclustermunitions.org.

International Campaign to Stop Rape and Gender Violence in Conflict, 1 Nicholas St - Suite 430, Ottawa, ONT - K1N 7B7, Canada (+1-613-569 8400) (fax 691 1419) (info@stoprapeinconflict.org) (www.stoprapeinconflict.org).

International Cities of Peace (CD), 1740 E Stroop Rd - Box 291-761, Dayton, OH 45429, USA (info@internationalcitiesofpeace.org) (www.internationalcitiesofpeace.org).

International Coalition to Ban Uranium Weapons [ICBUW] (AT DA), Bridge 5 Mill, 22a Beswick St, Ancoats, Manchester M4 7HR, Britain (+44-161-273 8293) (fax) (info@icbuw.org) (www.bandepleteduranium.org).

International Committee for Robot Arms Control [ICRAC] (AT DA), c/o Noel Sharkey, Department of Computer Science, University of Sheffield, Western Bank, Sheffield 10, Yorks, Britain (www.icrac.net). For peaceful use of robotics. Campaigns for regulation of robot weapons.

International Council of Voluntary Agencies / Conseil International des Agences Bénévoles [ICVA] (HR TW), 26-28 ave Giuseppe Motta, 1202 Genève, Switzerland (+41-22 950 9600) (secretariat@icvanetwork.org) (www.icvanetwork.org). Global network of humanitarian NGOs and human rights groups "promoting principled and effective humanitarian action".

International Fellowship of Reconciliation [IFOR] (RP IB), Postbus 1528, 3500 BM Utrecht, Netherlands (+31-30-303 9930) (office@ifor.org) (www.ifor.org).

International Humanist and Ethical Union [IHEU] (HR PO), 39 Moreland St, London EC1, Britain (+44-20-7490 8468) (office-iheu@iheu.org) (www.iheu.org). *International Humanist News*. In USA: +1-518-632 1040.

International Institute for Peace through Tourism / Institut International pour la Paix par le Tourisme [IIPT] (CD), 685 Cottage Club Rd - Unit 13, Stowe, VT 05672, USA (+1-802-253 8671) (fax 253 2645) (ljd@iipt.org) (www.iipt.org). Committed to making travel and tourism a global peace industry; believe that every traveller is potentially an ambassador for peace.

International Network of Engaged Buddhists [INEB] (FR TW EL HR), 666 Charoen Nakorn Rd (between Soi 20-22), Banglumpulang, Klong San, Bangkok 10600, Thailand (+66-2860 2194) (fax 2860 1277) (secretariat@inebnetwork.org) (www.inebnetwork.org).

International Network of Engineers and Scientists for Global Responsibility [INES] (IB), Marienstr 19-20, 10117 Berlin, Germany (+49-30-3199 6686) (fax 3199 6689) (office@inesglobal.net) (www.inesglobal.net).

International Network of Museums for Peace [INMP] (IB RE), Laan van Meerdervoort 70, 2517 AN Den Haag, Netherlands (+31-70-345 0202) (info@museumsfor-peace.org) (www.museumsfor-peace.org). Worldwide network of peace museums, gardens, and other peace-related sites, centres and institutions, which share the desire to build a culture of peace.

International Peace Bureau [IPB] (AT ND RE TW TR), Marienstr 19-20, 10117 Berlin, Germany (+49-30-1208 4549) (info@ipb-office.berlin) (www.ipb.org). *IPB News*. Main programme: disarmament for development. Work includes Global Campaign on Military Spending. Most broadly-based international peace networking body. Also office in Geneva; and GCOMS co-ordination office in Barcelona.

International Peace Initiative for Syria (CR PA RE), c/o Study Centre for Peace and Conflict Resolution, 7461 Stadtschlaining, Burg, Austria (info@peaceinsyria.org) (www.peaceinsyria.org). Opposes all military solutions. Stresses importance of a ceasefire and de-escalation, and of priority involvement of unarmed civil society in negotiations. Works with World Social Forum.

International Peace Research Association [IPRA] (RE), c/o Risk and Conflict Network, Dept of Media & Communication Design, Northumbria University, Newcastle-upon-Tyne NE1 8ST, Britain (+44-191-227 3567) (www.iprapeace.org).

International Physicians for the Prevention of Nuclear War [IPPNW] (ND RE TW), 339 Pleasant St - Third floor, Malden, MA 02148, USA (+1-617-440 1733) (ippnwbos@ippnw.org) (ippnw.org).

For explanation of codes and abbreviations, see introduction

INTERNATIONAL ORGANISATIONS

International Secretariat of Nuclear-Free Local Authorities (ND EL), c/o Nuclear-Free Local Authorities Secretariat, Manchester City Council, Town Hall, Manchester M60 3NY, Britain (+44-161-234 3244) (fax 234 3379) (s.morris4@manchester.gov.uk) (www.nuclearpolicy.info).

International Tibet Network (HR), c/o Tibet Society UK, 2 Baltic Place, London N1 5AQ, Britain (mail@tibetnetwork.org) (www.tibet-network.org). Formerly International Tibet Support Network. Links 180 groups around the world. Local Tibet support groups can also be found via www.tibet.org.

Mayors for Peace (CD ND DA), c/o Hiroshima Peace Culture Foundation, 1-5 Nakajima-cho, Naka-ku, Hiroshima 730-0811, Japan (+81-82-242 7821) (fax 242 7452) (mayorcon@pcf.city.hiroshima.jp) (www.mayorsforpeace.org). *Mayors for Peace Newsletter*.

Minority Rights Group International [MRG] (HR RE), 54 Commercial St, London E1, Britain (+44-20-7422 4200) (fax 7422 4201) (minority.rights@mrgmail.org) (www.minorityrights.org). *State of the World's Minorities*. Publishes reports, studies, training manuals, briefing papers. Europe office, Hungary (+36-1-327 7038). Africa office, Uganda (+256-31-226 6832).

Nansen Dialogue Network [NDN] (CR CD), Bjørntjerne Bjørnsonsgt 2, 2609 Lillehammer, Norway (+47-6126 5400) (fax 6126 5440) (contact@nansen-dialogue.net) (www.nansen-dialogue.net).

NATO Watch (DA ND), 6 chemin d'Houldizy-Le Pont, 79200 Gourge, France (+44-7887 782389) (idavis@natowatch.org) (natowatch.org). *Observatory*. Collates information about NATO. Provides regular briefings.

NGO Committee for Disarmament - Geneva (DA ND AT), c/o IPB, Rue de Zürich 41, 1201 Genève, Switzerland (+41-22 731 6429) (mailbox@ipb.org) (www.ipb.org).

No to War - No to NATO (RA DA ND), c/o Reiner Braun, IALANA, Marienstr 19-20, 10117 Berlin, Germany (+41-30-2065 4857) (fax 2065 3837) (info@no-to-nato.net) (www.no-to-nato.org). Co-ordination of groups in many NATO states. Organises actions against NATO events. Also c/o Arielle Denis, Mouvement de la Paix, in France (Arielle.Denis@mvtpaix.org).

Nonviolence International (IB PA), 4000 Albermarle St NW - Suite 401, Washington, DC 20016, USA (+1-202-244 0951) (info@nonviolenceinternational.net) (nonviolenceinternational.net). Links resource centres promoting use of nonviolent action. Has nonviolence promotion centre at UN (+1-212-971 9777).

Nonviolent Peaceforce [NP] (CR HR), 13 chemin de Levant - Bat A, 01210 Ferney Voltaire, France (+33-967 461948) (headoffice@nonviolentpeaceforce.org) (www.nonviolentpeaceforce.org). Offices in Belgium, and in USA (+1-612-871 0005).

Organisation for the Prohibition of Chemical Weapons [OPCW] (DA), Johan de Wittlaan 32, 2517 JR Den Haag, Netherlands (+31-70-416 3300) (fax 360 3535) (public.affairs@opcw.org) (www.opcw.org).

Organisation Mondiale Contre la Torture / World Organisation Against Torture [OMCT] (HR), CP 21, 1211 Genève 8, Switzerland (+41-22 809 4939) (fax 22 809 4929) (omct@omct.org) (www.omct.org). Co-ordinates SOS-Torture Network. Europe regional office, Belgium (+32-2 218 3719), (omcteurope@omct.org). Involves 280 organisations in 93 countries, linking local groups in countries where torture exists with activists elsewhere.

Orthodox Peace Fellowship [OPF] (FR), Kanisstr 5, 1811 GJ Alkmaar, Netherlands (+31-72-515 4180) (incommunion@gmail.com) (www.incommunion.org). *In Communion*.

Parliamentarians for Nuclear Non-proliferation and Disarmament [PNND] (ND), Basel Peace Office, University of Basel, Petersgraben 27, 4051 Basel, Switzerland (info@pnnd.org) (www.pnnd.org). *PNND Notes*. United Nations office, New York (+1-646-289 5170). Central Europe office, Prague, Czech Republic (info@praguvision.org). East Asia Office, Yokohama, Japan (office@pacepot.org). Helps parliamentarians engage in issues of nuclear non-proliferation and disarmament.

Pax Christi International (RP IB CD RE CR), Rue du Progrès 323, 1030 Bruxelles, Belgium (+32-2 502 5550) (fax 2 502 4626) (hello@paxchristi.net) (www.paxchristi.net). *Newsletter*. Network of autonomous organisations - Catholic.

Peace Boat (CD RE ND HR), B1 - 3-13-1 - Takadanobaba, Shinjuku-ku, Tokyo 169-0075, Japan (+81-3-3363 8047) (fax 3363 7562) (pbglobal@peaceboat.gr.jp) (www.peaceboat.org).

Peace Brigades International / Brigadas Internacionales de Paz / Brigades de Paix Internationales [PBI] (HR CD CR RE), Development House, 56-64 Leonard St, London EC2A 4LT, Britain (+44-20-7065 0775) (admin@peacebrigades.org) (www.peacebrigades.org). Projects in Colombia, Guatemala, Mexico, Honduras, Kenya, Nepal.

Peace Research Institute Oslo / Institutt for Fredsforskning [PRIO] (RE CR), PO Box 9229, Grønland, 0134 Oslo, Norway (+47-2254 7700) (fax 2254 7701)

INTERNATIONAL ORGANISATIONS

(info@prio.no) (www.prio.no). *Journal of Peace Research*; *Security Dialogue*. Journals from: SAGE Publications, 6 Bonhill St, London EC2, Britain (+44-20-7374 0645).

Peacebuilding Support Office of the United Nations (CR RE), UN Secretariat - 30th Floor, New York, NY 10017, USA (+1-212-963 9999) (www.un.org/en/peacebuilding). Formerly United Nations Peacebuilding Commission.

Privacy International (HR), 62 Britton St, London EC1, Britain (+44-20-3422 4321) (info@privacyinternational.org) (www.privacyinternational.org). For data protection, and control of surveillance.

Pugwash Conferences on Science and World Affairs (ND EL RE TW), 1211 Connecticut Ave NW - Suite 800, Washington, DC 20036, USA (+1-202-478 3440) (pugwashdc@aol.com) (pugwash.org). Offices also in Rome (+39-06-687 8376), Geneva (+41-22 907 3667), London (+44-20-7405 6661).

Quaker Council for European Affairs [QCEA] (SF HR PA EL AT), Square Ambiorix 50, 1000 Brussel, Belgium (+32-2 230 4935) (fax 2 230 6370) (office@qcea.org) (www.qcea.org). *Around Europe.*

Quaker UN Office - Geneva [QUNO] (SF HR TW EL CR), 13 Av du Mervelet, 1209 Genève, Switzerland (+41-22 748 4800) (fax 22 748 4819) (quno@quno.ch) (www.quno.org). *Geneva Reporter.*

Quaker UN Office - New York [QUNO] (SF), 777 UN Plaza, New York, NY 10017, USA (+1-212-682 2745) (fax 983 0034) (qunony@afsc.org) (www.quno.org/newyork).

Registry of World Citizens [WCR] (WF IB WP RE), 66 Bd Vincent Auriol, 75013 Paris, France (+33-14586 0358) (fax 241 784775) (abc@recim.org) (www.recim.org). Formerly World Citizen Registry.

Religions for Peace (RP IB RE CR TW), 777 United Nations Plaza, New York, NY 10017, USA (+1-212-687 2163) (fax 983 0098) (info@rfp.org) (religionsforpeace.org). Formerly World Conference of Religions for Peace. Regional offices in Asia, Europe, Latin America, Africa.

School Day of Non-Violence and Peace / Día Escolar de la No-Violencia y la Paz [DENIP] (RE), Apdo Postal 77, 11510 Puerto Real, Spain (ahimsadenip@yahoo.es) (denip.webcindario.com). (30 January, anniversary of Mahatma Gandhi's death).

Sea Shepherd (EL RA), 2226 Eastlake Ave E - No 45, Seattle, WA 98102-3419, USA (+1-212-220 2302) (fax 360-370 5651) (info@seashepherd.org) (www.seashepherd.org). Nature conservation on the high seas. European office: info@seashepherd.nl.

Search for Common Ground - Brussels Office (RE CD CR), Rue Belliard 205 - bte 13, 1040 Bruxelles, Belgium (+32-2 736 7262) (fax 2 732 3033) (brussels@sfcg.org) (www.sfcg.org). Conflict transformation projects in 34 countries. Washington DC Office (+1-202-265 4300); West Africa Office, Freetown (+232-22-223479).

Sennacieca Asocio Tutmonda - Worker Esperantists [SAT] (CD PA EL HR), 67 Av Gambetta, 75020 Paris, France (+33-14797 7190) (kontakto@satesperanto.org) (www.satesperanto.org). *Sennaciulo.*

Servas International [SI] (CD PO), c/o Jonny Sågänger, Reimersholmsgatan 47 - plan 0, 11740 Stockholm, Sweden (helpdesk@servas.org) (www.servas.org). World hospitality network for peace and goodwill. Building understanding by facilitating personal contacts between people of different nationalities.

Service Civil International - International Office [SCI] (WC PA TW PO HR), Belgiëlei 37, 2018 Antwerpen, Belgium (+32-3 226 5727) (fax 3 232 0344) (info@sciint.org) (www.sciint.org).

Sikh Human Rights Group (HR CR), 89 South Rd, Southall UB1, Middlesex, Britain (shrg@shrg.net) (shrg.net).

Statewatch (HR CD), 356 Holloway Rd, London N7 6PA, Britain (+44-20-7697 4266) (office@statewatch.org) (www.statewatch.org). Covers Europe. Critical research in fields of state, justice, home affairs, accountability, etc.

Stockholm International Peace Research Institute [SIPRI] (RE), Signalistgatan 9, 16972 Solna, Sweden (+46-8-655 9700) (sipri@sipri.org) (www.sipri.org). *SIPRI Yearbook.*

Third World Network [TWN] (TW), 131 Jalan Macalister, 10400 Penang, Malaysia (+60-4-226 6728) (fax 226 4505) (twn@twnetwork.org) (www.twn.my). *Third World Resurgence*; *Third World Network Features*. Latin America Secretariat: ITEM, Av 18 de Julio 2095/301, Montevideo 11200, Uruguay. Africa Secretariat: 9 Ollenu St, PO Box AN 19452, Accra-North, Ghana (fax +233-21-511188). Also publishes *South-North Development Monitor* (SUNS).

Transnational Institute [TNI] (HR ND RE TW EL), PO Box 14656, 1001 LD Amsterdam, Netherlands (+31-20-662 6608) (fax 675 7176) (tni@tni.org) (www.tni.org). *Transnational Institute Series*. Research in support of social movements.

UN Non-Governmental Liaison Service (New York Office) [UN-NGLS] (EL HR PO TW), Room DC1-1106, United Nations, New York, NY 10017, USA (+1-212-963 3125) (fax 963 8712) (info@un-ngls.org) (www.un-ngls.org).

INTERNATIONAL ORGANISATIONS

UNICEF, 3 United Nations Plaza, New York, NY 10017, USA (+1-212-326 7000) (fax 887 7465) (aaltamirano@unicef.org) (www.unicef.org)

United Nations [UN] (TW EL HR ND), UN Headquarters Building, New York, NY 10017, USA (+1-212-963 1234). (HQs of some of the UN's Specialised Agencies and Departments are also separately listed).

United Nations Department for Disarmament Affairs (AT CR ND DA), UN Headquarters Bldg (Rm DN25-12), New York, NY 10017, USA (+1-212-963 1570) (fax 963 4066) (www.un.org/disarmament).

United Nations Institute for Disarmament Research [UNIDIR] (RE), Palais des Nations, 1211 Genève 10, Switzerland (+41-22 917 1141) (fax 22 917 0176) (unidir@unog.ch) (www.unidir.org).

Universala Esperanto-Asocio [UEA] (HR CD PO), Nieuwe Binnenweg 176, 3015 BJ Rotterdam, Netherlands (+31-10-436 1044) (fax 436 1751) (uea@co.uea.org) (www.uea.org). *Esperanto*; *Kontakto*.

War Resisters' International [WRI] (PA RA HR TR CR), 5 Caledonian Rd, London N1 9DX, Britain (+44-20-7278 4040) (fax 7278 0444) (info@wri-irg.org) (wri-irg.org). *The Broken Rifle*; *CO Update*; *War Profiteers News*. Network of organisations of nonviolent activists, pacifists, conscientious objectors, etc. Also, tel +44-20-3355 2364.

Women Living Under Muslim Laws - International Solidarity Network [WLUML] (HR CD), PO Box 28455, London N19 5JT, Britain (+44-20-7263 0285) (fax 7561 9882) (wluml@wluml.org) (www.wluml.org). Arica and Middle East office: PO Box 5330, Dakar Fann, Dakar, Senegal (grefels@gmail.com). Asia office: PO Box 5192, Lahore, Pakistan (sgah@sgah.org.pk). Includes Violence is Not our Culture campaign (www.violenceisnotourculture.org).

Women's International League for Peace and Freedom [WILPF] (PA HR AT ND), CP 28, 1 rue de Varembé, 1211 Genève 20, Switzerland (+41-22 919 7080) (fax 22 919 7081) (secretariat@wilpf.ch) (www.wilpf.org). WILPF UN Office: 777 UN Plaza - 6th Floor, New York, NY 10017, USA (+1-212-682 1265) (fax 286 8211). Projects of UN office include (www.peacewomen.org) and (www.reachingcriticalwill.org).

World Federalist Movement - Institute for Global Polivy [WFM-IGP] (WF HR RE TW), 708 3rd Ave - Suite 1715, New York, NY 10017, USA (+1-212-599 1320) (fax 599 1332) (info@wfm-igp.org) (www.wfm-igp.org). Also: Bezuidenhoutseweg 99A, 2594 AC Den Haag, Netherlands (+31-70-363 4484).

World Federation of United Nations Associations / Fédération Mondiale des Associations pour les NU [WFUNA/FMANU] (TW HR), Palais des Nations - Room E4-2A, 1211 Genève 10, Switzerland (+41-22 917 3239) (info@wfuna.org) (www.wfuna.org). Also: 1 United Nations Plaza - Rm 1177, New York, NY 10017, USA (+1-212-963 5610) (wfunany@wfuna.org).

World Future Council Foundation (WF EL), Lilienstr 5-9, 20095 Hamburg, Germany (+49-40-3070 9140) (fax 3070 91414) (info@worldfuturecouncil.org) (www.worldfuturecouncil.org). Promotes sustainable future. Other offices: EU (+32-2 648 1852) (info.eu@worldfuturecouncil.org); UK (+44-20-7321 3810) (info.uk@worldfuturecouncil.org); USA (+1-202-547 9359) (info.us@worldfuturecouncil.org); Johannesburg (+27-11 726 1131).

World Information Service on Energy [WISE] (EL ND RA), Postbus 59636, 1040 LC Amsterdam, Netherlands (+31-20-612 6368) (info@wiseinternational.org) (www.wiseinternational.org). *WISE/NIRS Nuclear Monitor*. Grassroots-oriented anti-nuclear information. Works with NIRS in USA. Links with groups in Argentina, Austria, Czech Republic, India, Japan, Russia, Slovakia, South Africa, Sweden, Ukraine.

World Orchestra for Peace [WOP] (CD UN PO), c/o Charles Kaye, 26 Lyndale Ave, London NW2 2QA, Britain (+44-20-7317 8433) (ckconsult@compuserve.com) (www.worldorchestraforpeace.org). Also tel +44-7967-108974. Established 1995. Designated UNESCO Artist for Peace in 2010.

World Peace Council / Consejo Mondial de la Paz [WPC] (ND TW), Othonos St 10, 10557 Athinai, Greece (+30-210 3316 326) (fax 210 3251 576) (wpc@otenet.gr) (www.wpc-in.org).

World Service Authority [WSA] (WF HR PA CD), 5 Thomas Circle NW - Suite 300, Washington, DC 20005, USA (+1-202-638 2662) (fax 638 0638) (info@worldservice.org) (www.worldservice.org). *World Citizen News*.

World Student Christian Federation - Inter-Regional Office [WSCF] (TW RP HR), Ecumenical Centre, BP 2251, 1211 Genève 2, Switzerland (+41-22 791 6358) (fax 22 791 6221) (wscf@wscf.ch) (www.wscfglobal.org). *Federation News*; *Student World*.

Youth for Exchange and Understanding [YEU] (CD), Ave du Suffrage Universel 49, 1030 Bruxelles, Belgium (+32-2 649 2048) (fax) (info@yeu-international.org) (www.yeu-international.org). Also Portugal office (+351-289-813074).

AFGHANISTAN

Co-operation for Peace and Unity [CPAU] (RE HR CR), House 997, Second Street, Kolola Pushta Rd, Kabul (+93-700 278891) (info@cpau.org.af) (www.cpau.org.af). Promoting peace, justice, human rights.

Revolutionary Association of the Women of Afghanistan [RAWA] (HR), see under Pakistan.

Women, Peace & Security Research Institute [RIWPS] (RE), Taimani, Street 8 - House 43, Kabul (+93-792 615421) (info@riwps-afghanistan.org) (www.riwps-afghanistan.org).

ALBANIA

Fondacioni Shqiptar Zgjidhja e Konflikteve dhe Pajtimi i Mosmarrëveshjeve [AFCR] (RE CR), Rr "Him Kolli" - Pall PF Trade - Nr 5, Tiranë (+355-4-226 4681) (fax 226 4837) (mediationalb@abcom.al) (www.mediationalb.org). *Pajtimi.*

Komiteti Shqiptar i Helsinkit / Albanian Helsinki Committee (HR), Rr Brigada VIII - Pll Tekno Projekt - Shk 2 - Ap 10, Tiranë (+355-4-223 3671) (fax) (office@ahc.org.al) (www.ahc.org.al).

Partia e Gjelber - Albanian Green Party (EL), Rruga Bul Bajram Curri - Sh 1 - Shk 1 - Ap 4, Tiranë (+355-69-612 0150) (fax 4-223 8689) (pgj.office@gmail.com) (www.pgj.al).

Women's International League for Peace and Freedom - Albania (WL), Rruga Naim Fresheri - P 84 - Sh2 - Ap31, Tiranë (+355-42-2297938) (fax) (tkurtiqi@hotmail.com).

ANDORRA

Partit Verds d'Andorra (EL), Apartat de Correus 2136, Andorra la Vella AD500 (+376-363797) (andorraverds@gmail.com) (www.verds.ad). Green Party.

ANGOLA

Iniciativa Angolana Antimilitarista para os Direitos Humanos [IAADH] (WR HR), see under Germany (www.iaadh.de).

Search for Common Ground in Angola (CR CD), 15 rua D2 - Capolo II, Kilamba-Kiaxi, Luanda (angola@sfcg.org) (www.sfcg.org).

ARGENTINA

Greenpeace Argentina (GP), Zabala 3873, 1427 Buenos Aires (+54-11-4551 8811) (fax) (activismo@infogreenpeace.org.ar) (www.greenpeace.org/argentina).

AUSTRALIA

Act for Peace [AFP] (RP RE TW DA), c/o National Council of Churches in Australia, Locked Bag Q199, Sydney, NSW 1230 (+61-2-8259 0800) (www.actforpeace.org.au).

Alternatives to Violence Project (CR), c/o AVP(NSW), PO Box 161, Lane Cove, NSW 1595 (+61-2-9449 8415) (avpaus@avp.org.au) (www.avp.org.au).

Amnesty International Australia (AI), Locked Bag 23, Broadway, NSW 2007 (+61-2-8396 7600) (fax 9217 7663) (supporter@amnesty.org.au) (www.amnesty.org.au).

Anabaptist Association of Australia and New Zealand (RP), PO Box 738, Mona Vale, NSW 1660 (+61-2-8919 0367) (aaanz.info@gmail.com) (www.anabaptist.asn.au).

Anti-Nuclear Alliance of Western Australia [ANAWA] (ND EL), 5 King William St, Bayswater, WA 6053 (+61-8-9272 4252) (admin@anawa.org.au) (www.anawa.org.au).

Australian Anti-Bases Campaign Coalition [AABCC] (IB WP AT ND RA), PO Box A899, Sydney South, NSW 1235 (+61-2-9698 5617) (denis@anti-bases.org) (www.anti-bases.org).

Australian Nuclear Free Alliance (EL), c/o Friends of the Earth, PO Box 222, Fitzroy, Vic 3065 (+61-3-9419 8700) (fax 9416 2081) (anfacommittee@gmail.com) (www.anfa.org.au).

Centre for Peace Studies (RE EL SD), University of New England, Armidale, NSW 2351 (+61-2-6773 2442) (fax 6773 3350) (hware@une.edu.au) (www.une.edu.au/study/peace-studies). Organise annual Nonviolence Film Festival.

Christian Peacemaker Teams Australasia [CPTA] (RP RA CR), PO Box 738, Mona Vale, NSW 1660 (+61-2-9997 4632) (doug.hynd@netspeed.com.au). An initiative of various church groups.

Coalition for Justice & Peace in Palestine [CJPP] (HR), PO Box 144, Glebe, NSW 2037 (cjpp@coalitionforpalestine.org) (www.coalitionforpalestine.org).

Conflict Resolution Network [CRN] (CR UN RE), PO Box 1016, Chatswood, NSW 2057 (+61-2-9419 8500) (fax 9413 1148) (crn@crnhq.org) (www.crnhq.org).

Ecumenical Accompaniment Programme in Palestine and Israel - Australia (RP HR), c/o National Council of Churches in Australia, Locked Bag Q199, Sydney, NSW 1230 (+61-2-8259 0800) (www.ncca.org.au/eappi).

Friends of the Earth (FE RA PO), PO Box 222, Fitzroy, Vic 3065 (+61-3-9419 8700) (fax 9416 2081) (foe@foe.org.au) (www.foe.org.au).

Greenpeace Australia Pacific (GP), GPO Box 2622, Sydney, NSW 2001 (+61-2-9281 6100) (fax 9280 0380) (support.au@greenpeace.org) (www.greenpeace.org.au).

AUSTRALIA

Greens (WA) (EL HR DA), PO Box 3022, East Perth, WA 6892 (+61-8-9221 8333) (fax 9221 8433) (office@wa.greens.org.au) (www.wa.greens.org.au). *Green Issue.*

Independent and Peaceful Australia Network [IPAN] (PA DA), PO Box 573, Coorparoo, Qld 4151 (ipan.australia@gmail.com) (www.ipan.org.au). Opposes overseas military bases.

International Volunteers for Peace [IVP] (SC), 499 Elizabeth St, Surry Hills, NSW 2010 (+61-2-9699 1129) (fax 9318 0918) (admin@ivp.org.au) (www.ivp.org.au).

Medical Association for Prevention of War [MAPW] (IP), PO Box 1379, Carlton, Vic 3053 (+61-3-8344 1637) (fax 8344 1638) (mapw@mapw.org.au) (mapw.org.au). *Newsletter.*

Nonlethal Security for Peace Campaign (DA RE), PO Box 724, Avalon Beach, NSW 2107 (info@tamingwar.com) (www.nonlethalsecurityforpeace.com). Previously Non-Lethal Weapons for Peace Campaign.

Pace e Bene Australia [PeBA] (PA RP), 5/63 Roslyn St, Brighton, Vic 3186 (+61-3-9592 5247) (d.hess@ozemail.com.au) (www.pacebene.org). For nonviolence and cultural transformation.

Pax Christi (PC IB), PO Box 31, Carlton South, Vic 3053 (+61-3-9893 4946) (fax 9379 1711) (pax@paxchristi.org.au) (www.paxchristi.org.au). *Disarming Times.* Also NSW (+61-2-9550 3845).

People for Nuclear Disarmament - Western Australia [PND] (IB ND), 5 King William St, Bayswater, WA 6053 (+61-9-9272 4252) (jovall@iinet.net.au).

People's Charter to Create a Nonviolent World (PA TW EL), PO Box 68, Daylesford, Vic 3460 (flametree@riseup.net) (thepeoplesnonviolencecharter. wordpress.com).

Quaker Service Australia (SF TW), 119 Devonshire St, Surry Hills, NSW 2010 (+61-2-9698 9103) (fax 9225 9241) (administration@qsa.org.au) (www.qsa.org.au).

Religions for Peace Australia (RP), 71 Wellington St, Flemington, Vic 3031 (wcrpaust@iinet.net.au) (religionsforpeaceaustralia.org.au).

Reprieve Australia (HR), PO Box 4296, Melbourne, VIC 3001 (+61-3-9670 4108) (contact@reprieve.org.au) (www.reprieve.org.au). Campaigns against death penalty.

SafeGround (DA), PO Box 2143, Morphettville, SA 5043 (info@safeground.org.au) (safeground.org.au). Work to reduce impact of explosive remnants of war.

Schweik Action Wollongong (SD), PO Box U129, Wollongong, NSW 2500 (+61-2-4228 7860) (fax 4221 5341) (brian_martin@uow.edu.au) (www.bmartin.cc/others/SAW.html).

Servas Australia (SE), c/o Pam Webster, 2 Warili Rd, Frenchs Forest, 2076 (+61-2-9451 9669) (secretary@servas.org.au) (www.servas.org.au).

Society of Friends (SF), PO Box 556, Kenmore, Qld 4069 (ymsecretary@quakers.org.au) (www.quakers.org.au).

Tasmanian Quaker Peace & Justice Committee [TQPJC] (SF PA), PO Box 388, North Hobart, Tas 7002 (+61-400-925385).

War Resisters' League [WRL] (WR AL HR), PO Box 451, North Hobart, Tas 7002 (+61-3-6278 2380) (fax 6234 8209) (pdpjones@optusnet.com.au).

Women's International League for Peace and Freedom [WILPF] (WL ND), PO Box 345, Rundle Mall, Adelaide, SA 5000 (+61-8-8390 3456) (wilpfaustralia@wilpf.org.au) (www.wilpf.org.au). *Peace & Freedom.*

World Citizens Association (Australia) [WCAA] (WF), PO Box 6318, University of New South Wales, Sydney, NSW 1466 (C.Hamer@unsw.edu.au) (www.worldcitizens.com.au). *The Bulletin.*

AUSTRIA

Amnesty International Österreich (AI), MÖringgasse 10, 1150 Wien (+43-1-78008) (fax 780 0844) (office@amnesty.at) (www.amnesty.at).

Arbeitsgemeinschaft für Wehrdienstverweigerung, Gewaltfreiheit und Flüchtlingsbetreuung [ARGE Wien] (WR), Schotteng 3A/1/59, 1010 Wien (+43-1-535 9109) (fax 532 7416) (argewdv@verweigert.at) (www.verweigert.at).

Arbeitsgemeinschaft für Wehrdienstverweigerung, Gewaltfreiheit und Flüchtlingsbetreuung - ARGE Salzburg (WR SC), Argekultur, Josef Preis Allee 16, 5020 Salzburg (+43-662-847743) (arge-wdv@gmx.net) (verweigert.at).

Bürgermeister für den Frieden in Deutschland und Österreich (CD ND DA), see under Germany.

Begegnungszentrum für Aktive Gewaltlosigkeit / Centre for Encounter and Active Nonviolence [BFAG] (PA TW EL), Wolfgangerstr 26, 4820 Bad Ischl (+43-6132-24590) (info@begegnungszentrum.at) (www.begegnungszentrum.at). *Rundbrief.*

Die Grünen (EL AL PO), Rooseveltplatz 4-5, 1090 Wien (+43-1-2363 9980) (fax 526 9110) (bundesbuero@gruene.at) (www.gruene.at). Green Party.

Franz Jägerstätter House (PC), St Radegund 31, 5121 Ostermiething (+43-6278-8219) (pfarre.stradegund@dioezese-linz.at).

Internationaler VersÖhnungbund [IVB] (FR), Lederergasse 23/III/27, 1080 Wien (+43-1-408 5332) (fax) (office@versoehnungsbund.at) (www.versoehnungsbund.at). *Spinnrad.*

IPPNW Österreich [OMEGA] (IP), Schulgasse 40/17, 1180 Wien (+43-2988-6236) (office@ippnw.at) (www.ippnw.at).

Konfliktkultur (CR PO), Breitenfeldergasse 2/14, 1080 Wien (+43-699-1944 1313) (office@konfliktkultur.at) (www.konfliktkultur.at).

Österreichische Gesellschaft für Aussenpolitik und die Vereinten Nationen [OEGAVN] (UN), Reitschulgasse 2/2, Hofburg/Stallburg, 1010 Wien (+43-1-535 4627) (office@oegavn.org.at) (www.una-austria.org).

Österreichisches Netzwerk für Frieden und Gewaltfreiheit (RE), c/o IVB, Lederergasse 23/III/27, 1080 Wien (www.friedensnetzwerk.at).

Peace Museum Vienna (RÉ), Blutgasse 3/1, 1010 Wien (office@peacemuseumvienna.com) (www.peacemuseumvienna.com). Includes Windows for Peace project in city streets.

AZERBAIJAN

Azerbaijan Campaign to Ban Landmines [ACBL] (AT), 38 Sh Badalbeily St - Apt 2, Baku 1014 (+994-12-494 1458) (fax) (azerbaijan@icbl.org) (www.azcbl.org).

Azerbaycan Insan Huquqlarini Mudafie Merkezi / Human Rights Centre of Azerbaijan [AIHMM/HRCA] (HR), PO Box 31, Baku 1000 (+994-12-492 1369) (fax) (eldar.hrca@gmail.com) (penitentiary.ucoz.ru). *Human Rights in Azerbaijan.*

BAHRAIN

Bahrain Human Rights Society [BHRS] (HR), PO Box 20306, Manama (+973-1782 5425) (fax 1782 6836) (bhrs@bhrs.org) (www.bhrs.org).

BANGLADESH

Bangladesh Interreligious Council for Peace and Justice [BICPAJ] (FR IB PC CR EL), 14/20 Iqbal Rd, Mohammadpur, Dhaka 1207 (+880-2-914 1410) (fax 812 2010) (bicpaj@bijoy.net) (www.bicpaj.org).

Manush Manusher Jonnyo (HR EL CD PO TW), Nahar Peace Garden, 202/1 Tutpara Main Rd, Khulna Metro 9100 (fax +880-41-725071) (manusmanusherjonnyo@gmail.com). *Ideas for a Better Bangladesh.*

Service Civil International [SCI] (SC), 57/15 East Razabazar, Panthapath West, Dhaka 1215 (+880-2-935 3993) (scibangladesh@gmail.com) (scibangladesh.org).

BARBADOS

Barbados Inter-Religious Organisation [BIRO] (RP), c/o Roman Catholic Diocese of Bridgetown, PO Box 1223, Bridgetown (vincentblackett@hotmail.com). Affiliated to Religions for Peace International.

BELARUS

Alternativnaya Grazhdanskaya Sluzhba / Campaign for Alternative Civilian Service in Belarus [AGS] (HR PA), Bakinskaya Str 8-44, 220007 Minsk (+375-25-999 4699) (ags.belarus@gmail.com) (ags.by).

Belarusian Helsinki Committee (HR), Karl Liebknecht St 68 - off 1201, 220036 Minsk (+375-17-222 4800) (fax 222 4801) (office@belhelcom.org) (www.belhelcom.org).

Belrad Institute of Radiation Safety (EL), 2 Marusinsky - pereulok 27, Minsk 220053 (+375-17-289 0383) (fax 289 0384) (belrad@nsys.by) (www.belrad-institute.org).

Green Cross Belarus (EL TW DA CR), Oktiabrsky St 16 - Building 3, 220030 Minsk (+375-17-210 0062) (fax 227 1146) (gcb@greencross.by) (www.greencross.by).

BELGIUM

Abolition 2000 Belgium (ND), c/o Vredesactie, Patriottenstr 27, 2600 Berchem (+32-3-281 6839) (lene@vredesactie.be) (www.abolition2000.be).

ACAT - Belgique Francophone (HR), Quai aux Foins 53, 1000 Bruxelles (+32-2 223 0159) (fax) (a.cat.belgique@gmail.com) (www.acat-belgique-francophone.be). *ACAT-info.*

ACAT België-Vlaanderen (HR), Zevenkerken 4, 8200 Sint-Andries (+32-50 406132) (info@acat-belgie-vlaanderen.org) (www.acat-belgie-vlaanderen.org).

Agir pour la Paix (WR), 35 rue van Elewyck, Ixelles, 1050 Bruxelles (+32-2 648 5220) (info@agirpourlapaix.be) (agirpourlapaix.be).

Amis de la Terre / Friends of the Earth [AT] (FE PO), Rue Nanon 98, 5000 Namur (+32-81 390639) (contact@amisdelaterre.be) (www.amisdelaterre.be). *Saluterreliens.*

Amnesty International Belgique Francophone [AIBF] (AI), Rue Berckmans 9, 1060 Bruxelles (+32-2 538 8177) (fax 2 537 3729) (aibf@aibf.be) (www.amnesty.be). *Libertés!.*

Amnesty International Vlaanderen (AI), Kerkstr 156, 2060 Antwerpen (+32-3 271 1616) (fax 3 235 7812) (amnesty@aivl.be) (www.aivl.be).

Artsen Voor Vrede [AVV] (IP), c/o Hugo d'Aes, Van Stralenstr 10, 2060 Antwerpen (hugo.daes@skynet.be) (users.skynet.be/artsenvoorvrede). *Gezondheidszorg en Vredesvraagstukken.*

Association Médicale pour la Prévention de la Guerre Nucléaire [AMPGN] (IP), Av des Platanes 48, 4000 Liège (+32-4 252 2240) (H.Firket@ulg.ac.be) (www.ampgn.be).

BELGIUM

Belgian Campaign to Ban Landmines and Cluster Munitions (RE AT), c/o Handicap International - Policy Unit, Spastr 67, 1000 Brussel (+32-2 280 1601) (fax 2 230 6030) (info@handicap.be) (www.handicap.be).

Brigades de Paix Internationales [BPI/PBI] (HR CR CD RE), 23 rue Lt F Wampach, 1200 Bruxelles (+32-473 878136) (pbibelgium@scarlet.be) (www.pbibelgium.be). *Présence Internationale.*

Comité de Surveillance OTAN [CSO] (ND PA RE), rue des Cultivateurs 62, 1040 Bruxelles (+32-2 511 6310) (fax) (info@csotan.org) (www.csotan.org). *Alerte OTAN.* They keep an eye on NATO.

Commission Justice et Paix - Belgique francophone (RP), Rue Maurice Liétart 31/6, 1150 Bruxelles (+32-2 738 0801) (fax 2 738 0800) (info@justicepaix.be) (www.justicepaix.be).

Flemish War and Peace Museum (RE), Ijzertoren, Ijzerdijk 49, 8600 Diksmuide (+32-51 500286) (info@aandeijzer.be) (www.museumaandeijzer.be).

Friends of the Earth (Flanders & Brussels) (FE ND HR), Maria-Hendrikaplein 5-6, 9000 Gent (+32-9 242 8752) (fax 9 242 8751) (contact@motherearth.org) (www.motherearth.org). *Bulletin.*

Greenpeace (GP), Haachtsesteenweg 159, 1030 Brussel (+32-2 274 0200) (fax 2 274 0230) (info.be@greenpeace.org) (www.greenpeace.org/belgium).

Groupe Interconfessionnel de la Réconciliation / Kinshasa [GIR] (FR), Route de Longchamp 26, 1348 Louvain-la-Neuve (buangajos@hotmail.com).

I Stop the Arms Trade (AT RA PA), c/o Vredesactie, Patriottenstr 27, 2600 Berchem (+32-3 281 6839) (ikstopwapenhandel@vredesactie.be) (ikstopwapenhandel.eu). Non-violent direct action against EU arms trade.

Moeders voor Vrede / Mères pour la Paix / Mothers for Peace, Grote Markt 34, 8900 Ieper (+32-483 599395) (info@mothersfor-peace.be) (www.mothersforpeace.be).

Pax Christi Vlaanderen [PCV] (PC RE CD ND CR), Italiëlei 98A, 2000 Antwerpen (+32-3 225 1000) (fax 3 225 0799) (paxchristi@paxchristi.be) (www.paxchristi.be). *Koerier.*

Pax Christi Wallonie-Bruxelles [PCWB] (PC), Rue Maurice Liétart 31/1, 1150 Bruxelles (+32-2 738 0804) (fax 2 738 0800) (info@paxchristiwb.be) (www.paxchristiwb.be). *Signes des Temps.*

Register van Wereldburgers / Registry of World Citizens [RW] (WF PA TW), Vredestr 65, 2540 Hove (+32-3 455 7763) (verstraeten.jean@belgacom.net) (www.recim.org/cdm). *Overleven door Wereldrecht / Survival by World Law.*

Religions for Peace - Belgium (RP), Av de la Reine 7, 1030 Bruxelles (fmdali@wcrp.be).

Say No (PA), A Beernaerstr 28a, 1170 Brussel (+32-497 934716) (info@desertie.be) (www.sayno.be). Anti-militarist choral project.

Servas - Belgium & Luxembourg (SE), c/o Rita Dessauvage, Kloosterweg 30, 1652 Beersel-Alsemberg (belgium@servas.org) (belgium.servas.org).

Sortir de la Violence [SDV] (FR CR RE), Blvd du Souverain 199, 1160 Bruxelles (+32-2 679 0644) (info@sortirdelaviolence.org) (www.sortirdelaviolence.org).

VIA (SC WC), Belgiëlei 37, 2018 Antwerpen (+32-3 707 1614) (via@viavzw.be) (www.viavzw.be).

Vlaams Vredesinstituut / Flemish Peace Institute (RE), Leuvenseweg 86, 1000 Brussel (+32-2 552 4591) (fax 2 552 4408) (vredesinstituut@vlaamsparlement.be) (www.vlaamsvredesinstituut.eu). Also (www.flemishpeaceinstitute.eu).

Vredesactie (WR AT ND), Patriottenstr 27, 2600 Berchem, Antwerpen (+32-3 281 6839) (contact@vredesactie.be) (www.vredesactie.be). *Vredesactie.*

Vrouwen in 't Zwart / Femmes en Noir / Women in Black [WiB] (PA DA HR), c/o Ria Convents, Vismarkt 8, 3000 Leuven (+32-16 291314) (marianne.vandegoorberg@telnet.be) (snellings.telenet.be/womeninblackleuven).

BERMUDA

Amnesty International Bermuda (AI), PO Box HM 2136, Hamilton HM JX (+1441-296 3249) (fax) (director@amnestybermuda.org).

BHUTAN

People's Forum for Human Rights (HR), see under Nepal.

BOSNIA-HERZEGOVINA

Centar za Nenasilnu Akciju / Centre for Nonviolent Action [CNA] (CD CR PA RE), Kranjceviceva 33, 71000 Sarajevo (+387-3326 0876) (fax 3326 0875) (cna.sarajevo@nenasilje.org) (www.nenasilje.org). See also in Serbia.

Medjureligijsko Vieće u BiH / Interreligiouis Council in Bosnia-Herzegovina [MRV] (RP), Ferhadija 16/1, 71000 Sarajevo (+387-3366 6776) (fax 3355 0060) (office@mrv.ba) (www.mrv.ba).

Nansen Dialogue Centre Mostar [NDC Mostar] (CR), Alekse Šantića/Tvrtka Miloša 19, 80000 Mostar (+387-36-327459) (fax 327458) (ndc-mostar@nansen-dialogue.net) (nansen-dialogue.net/ndcmostar).

Nansen Dialogue Centre Sarajevo [NDC Sarajevo] (CR), Hakije Kulenovića 10, 71000 Sarajevo (+387-33-556846) (fax 556845) (ndcsarajevo@nansen-dialogue.net) (www.ndcsarajevo.org).

BOTSWANA

Society of Friends (Quakers) (SF), c/o Shelagh Willet, Box 20166, Gaborone (+267-394 7147) (willet.shelagh@botsnet.bw).

BRAZIL

ACAT Brasil (HR), Praça Clovis Bevilaqua 357 - sala 701, 01018-001 São Paulo - SP (+55-11-3101 6084) (fax) (acatbrasil.international@gmail.com). Affiliated to FIACAT.

Associação das Nações Unidas - Brasil [ANUBRA] (UN), Av Brigadeiro Faria Lima 1485 - North Tower - 19th Floor, 01452-002 São Paulo - SP (+55-11-3094 7984) (fax) (unab@unab.org.br) (www.unab.org.br).

Centro Brasileiro de Solidariedade aos Povos e Luta pela Paz [CEBRAPAZ] (WP CD SD ND), Rua Conselheiro Crispiniano 97 - sala 1, RepÚblica, 01037-001 São Paulo - SP (+55-11-3223 3469) (cebrapaz@uol.com.br) (cebrapaz.org.br).

Commissão Pastoral da Terra [CPT] (PC), Edifício Dom Abel - 1º andar, Rua 19 - Nº 35, 74030-090 Centro Goiânia, Goiás (+55-62-4008 6466) (fax 4008 6405) (cpt@cptnacional.org.br) (www.cptnacional.org.br).

Green Cross Brazil (EL TW DA HR), Centro Empresarial Brasilia - SRTVS - Q 701 - Bloco A - Salas 311 e 31, 70340-907 Brasilia (+55-61-3226 4613) (greencrossbrasil.gcb@gmail.com) (gcint.org.br).

Instituto Sou da Paz (CR DA), Rua Luis Murat 260 - VI, Madalena, 05436-050 São Paulo - SP (+55-11-3093 7333) (fax) (atendimento@soudapaz.org) (www.soudapaz.org).

Serviço de Paz [SERPAZ] (RE DA CR), Rua 1º de Março 776 - sala 4 - Centro, 93010-210 São Leopoldo - RS (+55-51-3592 6106) (fax 2111 1411) (serpaz@serpaz.org.br) (www.serpaz.org.br).

Serviço Voluntário Internacional [SVI-Brasil] (SC), Rua Ribeiro Junqueira 161 - SI 3, Mangabeiras, Belo Horizonte - MG (+55-11-99493 1794) (pedro@svibrasil.org) (www.svibrasil.org).

BRITAIN

38 Degrees (EL HR TW TW), Room 134, 40 Bowling Green Lane, London EC1 (+44-20-7970 6023) (emailtheteam@38degrees.org.uk) (www.38degrees.org.uk). Organises internet lobbying on progressive issues.

Abolition 2000 UK (ND), 162 Holloway Rd, London N7 (mail@abolition2000uk.org) (www.abolition2000uk.org).

Acronym Institute for Disarmament Diplomacy (RE), Werks Central, 15-17 Middle St, Brighton BN1, Sussex (+44-20-7503 8857) (info@acronym.org.uk) (acronym.org.uk).

Action by Christians Against Torture [ACAT-UK] (HR), c/o 19 The Square, Knowle Park, Bristol BS4 (+44-117-971 0379) (uk.acat@gmail.com) (www.acatuk.org.uk). Newsletter.

Action for Southern Africa [ACTSA] (TW HR), Headland House, 308-312 Gray's Inn Rd, London WC1 (+44-20-7186 0750) (fax 7931 9398) (info@actsa.org) (www.actsa.org).

Action on Armed Violence (AT DA TW HR), 405 Mile End Rd, Bow, London E3 (info@aoav.org.uk) (aoav.org.uk).

Ahmadiyya Muslim Community (RP HR), c/o Baitul Futuh Mosque, 181 London Rd, Morden, Surrey SM4 (+44-333-240 0490) (enquiries@ahmadiyya.org.uk) (Ahmadiyya.org.uk). Anti-violence and pro freedom of thought group.

Aldermaston Women's Peace Camp(aign) [AWPC] (ND RA), c/o 8 Millar House, Merchants Rd, Bristol BS8 4HA (info@aldermaston.net) (www.aldermaston.net). Monthly Aldermaston peace camps; and other actions.

All-Party Parliamentary Group on Drones (DA), c/o Tom Watson MP, House of Commons, London SW1 (+44-20-7219 8123).

Alternatives to Violence Project - Britain [AVP Britain] (CR PO), 28 Charles Sq, London N1 6HT (+44-20-7324 4755) (info@avpbritain.org.uk) (www.avpbritain.org.uk).

Amnesty International - UK Section [AIUK] (AI), Human Rights Action Centre, 17-25 New Inn Yard, London EC2A 3EA (+44-20-7033 1500) (fax 7033 1503) (info@amnesty.org.uk) (www.amnesty.org.uk).

Anabaptist Network (RP), PO Box 68073, London N22 9HS (admin@anabaptistnetwork.com) (www.anabaptistnetwork.com).

Anglican Pacifist Fellowship [APF] (IB RP PA), Peace House, 19 Paradise St, Oxford OX1 1LD (enquiries@anglicanpeacemaker.org.uk) (www.anglicanpeacemaker.org.uk). The Anglican Peacemaker.

At Ease (HR), Bunhill Fields Meeting House, Quaker Court, Banner St, London EC1Y 8QQ (+44-20-7490 5223) (info@atease.org.uk) (www.atease.org.uk). Advice, counselling for military personnel.

Baby Milk Action (TW PO EL), 4 Brooklands Ave, Cambridge CB2 8BB (+44-1223-464420) (info@babymilkaction.org) (www.babymilkaction.org). BMA Update.

Bahá'í Community UK (RP), 27 Rutland Gate, London SW7 1DP (+44-20-7584 2566) (fax 7584 9402) (opa@bahai.org.uk) (www.bahai.org.uk).

Balkans Peace Park Project - UK Committee [B3P] (CD EL), c/o Rylstone Lodge, Rylstone, Skipton BD23 6LH, N Yorks (+44-1756-730231) (j.dyer@leeds.ac.uk) (www.balkanspeacepark.org).

Baptist Peace Fellowship [BPF] (FR), c/o 21 Kingshill, Cirencester GL7 1DE, Gloucestershire (bobgardiner@yahoo.co.uk) (www.baptist-peace.org.uk). *BPF Newsletter.*

Before You Sign Up, 11 Manor Rd, Stratford-upon-Avon, Warwickshire CV37 (info@beforeyousignup.info) (www.beforeyousignup.info). For people thinking of joining the armed forces.

Bertrand Russell Peace Foundation [BRPF] (RE PA ND), Russell House, Bulwell Lane, Nottingham NG6 0BT (+44-115-978 4504) (fax 942 0433) (elfeuro@compuserve.com) (www.russfound.org). *The Spokesman.*

Bloomsbury Ad Hoc Committee [BADHOC] (EL HR PA), c/o 26 Museum Chambers, Little Russell St, London WC1A 8PD (badhoc@activist.com).

Bradford University Department of Peace Studies (RE CR TW), Bradford BD7 1DP, West Yorks (+44-1274-235235) (fax 235240) (www.brad.ac.uk/acad/peace/).

Brighton Peace & Environment Centre [BPEC] (RE EL), 39-41 Surrey St, Brighton BN1, Sussex (+44-1273-766610) (info@bpec.org) (www.bpec.org).

British American Security Information Council [BASIC] (RE AT ND), 3 Whitehall Court, London SW1 (+44-20-7766 3461) (basicuk@basicint.org) (www.basicint.org). *BASIC Reports.*

Building Bridges for Peace (CR), c/o 2 Crossways, Cott Lane, Dartington, Totnes TQ9 6HE, Devon (info@buildingbridgesforpeace.org) (www.buildingbridgesforpeace.org). Conflict transformation through empathy.

Campaign Against Arms Trade [CAAT] (AT IB RA), Unit 4, 5-7 Wells Terrace, London N4 3JU (+44-20-7281 0297) (enquiries@caat.org.uk) (www.caat.org.uk). *CAAT News.*

Campaign against Climate Change [CCC] (EL RA), Top Floor, 5 Caledonian Rd, London N1 9DX (+44-20-7833 9311) (info@campaignccc.org) (www.campaignccc.org).

Campaign Against Criminalising Communities [CAMPACC] (HR), c/o 44 Ainger Rd, London NW3 (+44-20-7586 5892) (estella24@tiscali.co.uk) (www.campacc.org.uk).

Campaign Against Depleted Uranium [CADU] (EL DA), Bridge 5 Mill, 22a Beswick St, Ancoats, Manchester M4 7HR (+44-161-273 8293) (fax) (info@cadu.org.uk) (www.cadu.org.uk).

Campaign for a Nuclear-Free Middle East [CNFME] (ND), Mordechai Vanunu House, 162 Holloway Rd, London N7 8DQ (+44-20-8672 9698) (david.lrcnd@cnduk.org).

Campaign for Earth Federation / World Federalist Party (WF), c/o Ian Hackett, 1 Kenilworth Rd, London W5 5PB (+44-20-8579 7706) (worldfederalistparty@gmail.com) (www.federalunion.org.uk).

Campaign for Homosexual Equality [CHE] (HR), c/o 86 Caledonian Rd, London N1 9DN (+44-7941-914340) (info@c-h-e.org.uk) (www.c-h-e.org.uk).

Campaign for Human Rights in Turkey (HR), c/o Turkish & Kurdish Community Centre, Former Library, Howard Rd, London N16 8PU (+44-20-7275 8440) (fax 7275 7245).

Campaign for Nuclear Disarmament [CND] (IB ND RA RE), 162 Holloway Rd, London N7 8DQ (+44-20-7700 2393) (enquiries@cnduk.org) (www.cnduk.org). *Campaign!.*

Campaign for Nuclear Disarmament Cymru / Yr Ymgyrch dros Ddiarfogi Niwclear [CND Cymru] (ND RA AT DA), c/o 72 Heol Gwyn, Yr Alltwen, Pontardawe SA8 3AN (+44-1792-830330) (heddwch@cndcymru.org) (www.cndcymru.org). *Heddwch.*

Campaign for Press and Broadcasting Freedom [CPBF] (HR), 2nd floor, 23 Orford Rd, Walthamstow, London E17 9NL (freepress@cpbf.org.uk) (www.cpbf.org.uk). *Free Press.*

Campaign for the Accountability of American Bases [CAAB] (ND PA RA), 59 Swarcliffe Rd, Harrogate HG1, Yorks (+44-1423-884076) (mail@caab.corner.org.uk) (www.caab.org.uk).

Campaign Opposing Police Surveillance [COPS] (HR RA), c/o Haldane Society of Socialist Lawyers, PO Box 64195, London WC1A 9FD (campaignopposingpolicesurveillance.com).

Centre for Alternative Technology / Canolfan y Dechnoleg Amgen [CAT] (EL PO AL), Machynlleth, Powys SY20 9AZ (+44-1654-705950) (fax 702782) (info@cat.org.uk) (www.cat.org.uk). *Clean Slate.*

Centre for Global Education York (HR TW), York St John University, Lord Mayor's Walk, York YO31 7EX (+44-1904-876839) (fax 612512) (cge@yorksj.ac.uk) (www.centreforglobaleducation.org).

Centre for International Peacebuilding (CR RE TW EL), The White House, 46 High St, Buntingford, Herts SG9 9AH (+44-1763-272662) (eirwenharbottle@gmail.com).

Centre for Trust, Peace and Social Relations [CTPSR] (RE), 5 Innovation Village, Coventry University Technology Park, Cheetah Rd, Coventry CV1 2TT (+44-24-7765 1182) (info.ctpsr@coventry.ac.uk) (www.coventry.ac.uk).

Chernobyl Children's Project (UK) (PO EL CD), Kinder House, Fitzalan St, Glossop SK13, Derbyshire (+44-1457-863534) (ccprojectuk@gmail.com) (www.chernobyl-children.org.uk).

Children are Unbeatable! Alliance (HR), 125-127 Westminster Business Square, 1-45 Durham St, London SE11 (+44-20-7713 0569) (info@endcorporalpunishment.org) (www.childrenareunbeatable.org.uk). For abolition of all physical punishment.

Children of Peace (CR HR), 1st Floor, The Roller Mill, Mill Lane, Uckfield TN22 5AA, Sussex (+44-1825-768074) (info@childrenofpeace.org.uk) (www.childrenofpeace.org.uk). Charity working in Israel, Palestine, Jordan.

Christian Aid (TW), 35-41 Lower Marsh, London SE1 (+44-20-7620 4444) (fax 7620 0719) (info@christian-aid.org) (www.christianaid.org.uk).

Christian Campaign for Nuclear Disarmament [CCND] (ND RP), 162 Holloway Rd, London N7 8DQ (+44-20-7700 4200) (fax 7700 2357) (christians@cnduk.org) (www.christiancnd.org.uk). *Ploughshare.*

Christian International Peace Service [CHIPS] (RP CR PO EL), 17 Hopton House, Loughborough Estate, London SW9 7SP (+44-20-7078 7439) (info@chipspeace.org) (www.chipspeace.org).

Church & Peace (RP CR RE), 39 Postwood Green, Hertford Heath SG13 7QJ (+44-1992-416442) (IntlOffice@church-and-peace.org) (www.church-and-peace.org).

City to Sea (EL PO), 5 York Court, Wilder St, Bristol BS2 (www.citytosea.org.uk). Campaign to stop plastic pollution.

Clergy Against Nuclear Arms [CANA] (RP ND), c/o St Michael's, Marston Rd, Oxford (+44-1243-373611) (djfpeace@gmail.com).

Climate Outreach (EL), The Old Music Hall, 106-108 Cowley Rd, Oxford OX4 1JE (+44-1865-403334) (info@climateoutreach.org) (climateoutreach.org). Formerly Climate Outreach and Information Network.

Close Capenhurst Campaign (EL), c/o News From Nowhere, 96 Bold St, Liverpool L1 (closecapenhurst@gmail.com) (www.close-capenhurst.org.uk). Opposes uranium enrichment plant in Cheshire.

Co-operation Ireland (GB) (CD), Windy Ridge, Courtlands Hill, Pangbourne RG8, Berkshire (+44-118-976 7790) (fax) (murphy992@btinternet.com) (www.cooperationireland.org).

Commonweal Collection (RE AL PA EL), c/o J B Priestley Library, Bradford University, Bradford BD7 1DP, Yorks (+44-1274-233404) (commonweal@riseup.net) (bradford.ac.uk/library/libraries-and-collections/). Peace library.

Community for Reconciliation [CfR] (RP), Barnes Close, Chadwich, Malthouse Lane, Bromsgrove, Worcs B61 0RA (+44-1562-710231) (fax 710278) (cfrenquiry@aol.com) (www.cfrbarnesclose.co.uk). *Newslink.*

Conciliation Resources (CR), 173 Upper St, Islington, London N1 1RG (+44-20-7359 7728) (cr@c-r.org) (www.c-r.org). *Accord.*

Concord Media (PA EL TW), 22 Hines Rd, Ipswich IP3 9BG, Suffolk (+44-1473-726012) (sales@concordmedia.org.uk) (www.concordmedia.org.uk).

Conflict Research Society [CRS] (RE), c/o Hugh Miall, 45 Ethelbert Rd, Canterbury CT1 3NF, Kent (conflictresearchsociety@kent.ac.uk) (www.conflictresearchsociety.org.uk).

Conscience - Taxes for Peace not War (TR WR HR), 17 North Square, Hampstead Garden Suburb, London NW11 (+44-20-3515 9132) (campaign@conscienceonline.org.uk) (www.conscienceonline.org.uk). *Conscience Update.*

Conway Hall Ethical Society (HR RE), Conway Hall, Red Lion Sq, London WC1 4RL (+44-20-7405 1818) (admin@conwayhall.org.uk) (www.conwayhall.org.uk). *Ethical Record.* Formerly South Place Ethical Society.

Cord (TW CR), Floor 9, Eaton House, 1 Eaton Rd, Coventry CV1 2FJ (+44-24-7708 7777) (info@cord.org.uk) (www.cord.org.uk). International peacebuilding charity.

Corporate Watch (EL RA AL), c/o Freedom Press, Angel Alley, 84b Whitechapel High St, London E1 7QX (+44-20-7426 0005) (contact@corporatewatch.org) (www.corporatewatch.org). *News Update.*

Cross-Party Group on Nuclear Disarmament (ND), c/o Bill Kidd, M5.08, Scottish Parliament, Edinburgh EH99 1SP (+44-131-348 5688) (Bill.Kidd.msp@scottish.parliament.uk).

Cuba Solidarity Campaign (TW WC), c/o UNITE, 33-37 Moreland St, London EC1V 8BB (+44-20-7490 5715) (fax 7490 3556) (office@cuba-solidarity.org.uk) (www.cuba-solidarity.org.uk). *Cuba Si.*

Cumbrians Opposed to a Radioactive Environment [CORE] (EL), Dry Hall, Broughton Mills, Broughton-in-Furness, Cumbria LA20 (+44-1229-716523) (fax) (www.corecumbria.co.uk).

Cymdeithas y Cymod / FoR Wales (FR PA CR), 3 Tai Minffordd, Rhostryfan, Caernarfon, Gwynedd LL54 7NF (+44-1286-830913) (cymdeithasycymod@btinternet.com) (www.cymdeithasycymod.org.uk). *Cymod.*

Cymru dros Heddwch / Wales for Peace (RE DA), c/o Welsh Centre for International Affairs, Temple of Peace, Cathays Park, Cardiff CF10 (+44-29-2082 1051) (walesforpeace@wcia.org.uk) (www.walesforpeace.org). Partnership of 10 organisations.

Darvell Bruderhof (RP PA PO), Brightling Rd, Robertsbridge, Sussex TN32 5DR (+44-1580-883330) (darvell@bruderhof.com) (www.bruderhof.com). Anabaptist community.

Defend Free Speech Campaign (HR), c/o National Secular Society, 25 Re Lion Sq, London WC1 (admin@defendfreespeech.org.uk) (defendfreespeech.org.uk). Opposing government plan to ban "extremist" speech.

Defend the Right to Protest [DTRTP] (HR), BM DTRTP, London WC1N 3XX (+44-1661-881894) (info@edfendtherighttoprotest.org) (www.defendtherighttoprotest.org).

Drone Campaign Network (DA), c/o Peace House, 19 Paradise St, Oxford OX1 (DroneCampaignNetwork@riseup.net) (www.dronecampaignnetwork.org). Network of organisations and academics.

Drone Wars UK (DA HR), c/o FoR, 19 Paradise St, Oxford OX1 (chris@dronewars.net) (www.dronewars.net). Opposes growing British use of armed drones.

East London Against the Arms Fair [ELAAF] (AT), c/o Garden Cafe, 7 Cundy Rd, Custom House, London E16 (elaaf@hotmail.co.uk) (elaaf.org). Opposing regular massive arms fair in Docklands.

Economic Issues Programme of the Society of Friends (SF HR EL), QPSW, Friends House, 175 Euston Rd, London NW1 2BJ (+44-20-7663 1000) (suzannei@quaker.org.uk) (www.quaker.org.uk/economic-jcutice). *Earth & Economy newsletter.*

Ecumenical Accompaniment Programme in Palestine and Israel - British and Irish Group [EAPPI] (RP HR SF SD), c/o QPSW, Friends House, 173 Euston Rd, London NW1 2BJ (+44-20-7663 1144) (eappi@quaker.org.uk) (www.quaker.org.uk/eappi).

Edinburgh Peace and Justice Centre (CR ND PA RE HR), 5 Upper Bow, Edinburgh EH1 2JN (+44-131-629 1058) (contact@peaceandjustice.org.uk) (peaceandjustice.org.uk). *Peace and Justice News.* Promotes nonviolence, conflict resolution.

Egypt Solidarity Initiative (HR), c/o MENA Solidarity Network, Unit 193, 15-17 Caledonian Rd, London N1 (campaign@egyptsolidarityinitiative.net) (egyptsolidarityinitiative.org).

Ekklesia (RP RE), 235 Shaftesbury Ave, London WC2 (+44-20-7836 3930) (info@ekklesia.co.uk) (www.ekklesia.co.uk).

End Violence Against Women Coalition (HR), 17-25 New Inn Yard, London EC2 (+44-20-7033 1559) (admin@evaw.org.uk) (www.endviolenceagainstwomen.org.uk).

Environmental Investigation Agency [EIA] (EL), 62/63 Upper St, London N1 (+44-20-7354 7960) (ukinfo@eia-international.org) (www.eia-international.org). Also operates in USA.

Environmental Network for Central America [ENCA] (EL HR), c/o Janet Bye, 5 St Edmund's Place, Ipswich IP1 (+44-20-8769 0492) (enca.info@gmail.com) (www.enca.org.uk). *ENCA.* Works with affected communities.

Equity and Peace (CR), c/o 9 The Arcade, Belsay, Northumberland NE20 (+44-1661-881894) (www.equityandpeace.com).

Esperanto-Asocio de Britio [EAB] (PO HR), Esperanto House, Station Rd, Barlaston, Stoke-on-Trent, Staffs ST12 9DE (+44-1782-372141) (eab@esperanto.org.uk) (www.esperanto.org.uk). *EAB Update; La Brita Esperantisto.*

Ethical Consumer Research Association (EL PO AL), Unit 21, 41 Old Birley St, Manchester M15 (+44-161-226 2929) (fax 226 6277) (enquiries@ethicalconsumer.org) (www.ethicalconsumer.org). *Ethical Consumer.*

EuroPal Forum (HR), 21 Chalton St, London NW1 1JD (+44-20-3289 6057) (admin@europalforum.org) (europalforum.org.uk). Mobilises in support of Palestinian rights.

Faslane Peace Camp (ND RA AL), Shandon, Helensburgh, Dunbartonshire, G84 8NT (+44-1436-820901) (faslane30@gmail.com) (faslanepeacecamp.wordpress.com).

Fellowship of Reconciliation [FoR] (FR), Peace House, 19 Paradise St, Oxford OX1 1LD (+44-1865-250781) (office@for.org.uk) (www.for.org.uk). *Peacelinks; Peace by Peace.* Covers England and Scotland.

Fitnah - Movement for Women's Liberation (HR), BM Box 1919, London WC1N 3XX (fitnah.movement@gmail.com) (www.fitnah.org). *Fitnah.* Opposes misogynist cultural and religious customs.

Fly Kites Not Drones (CD HR), c/o VCNV-UK, 31 Carisbrooke Rd, St Leonards-on-Sea TN38, Sussex (kitesnotdrones@gmail.com) (www.flykitesnotdrones.org). Non-violence project for young people.

ForcesWatch (PA HR RE), 5 Caledonian Rd, London N1 (+44-20-7837 2822) (office@forceswatch.net) (www.forceswatch.net).

Forum for the Future (EL), 9 Imperial Sq, Cheltenham, Glos GL50 1QB (+44-1242-262737) (info@forumforthefuture.org) (www.forumforthefuture.org). Charity working for sustainability.

Free Tibet Campaign (HR TW EL), 28 Charles Sq, London N1 6HT (+44-20-7324 4605) (fax 7324 4606) (mail@freetibet.org) (www.freetibet.org). *Free Tibet.*

Friends of Lebanon [FOL] (CR RE SD), Unit 35, 61 Praed St, London W2 1NS (+44-1923-606385) (mail@friendsoflebanon.org) (www.friendsoflebanon.org).

Friends of the Earth - England, Wales and Northern Ireland [FOE] (FE PO), The Printworks, 1st Floor, 139 Clapham Rd, London SW9 0HP (+44-20-7490 1555) (info@foe.co.uk) (www.foe.co.uk). *Earthmatters.*

Friends of the Earth Cymru / Cyfeillion y Ddaear Cymru (FE), 33 The Balcony, Castle Arcade, Cardiff CF10 1BY (+44-29-2022 9577) (cymru@foe.co.uk) (www.foecymru.co.uk).

Friends of the Earth Scotland (FE), Thorn House, 5 Rose St, Edinburgh EH2 2PR (+44-131-243 2700) (fax 243 2725) (info@foe-scotland.org.uk) (www.foe-scotland.org.uk). *What on Earth.*

Gandhi Foundation (HR RE PO), Kingsley Hall, Powis Rd, Bromley-by-Bow, London E3 3HJ (contact@gandhifoundation.org) (www.gandhifoundation.org). *The Gandhi Way.*

Gender Action for Peace and Security UK [GAPS] (HR RE), c/o Womankind Worldwide, Development House, 56-64 Leonard St, London EC2A 4LT (+44-20-7549 0772) (fax 7549 0361) (nowomennopeace@gaps-uk.org) (www.gaps-uk.org). Network of organisations and individual experts.

GeneWatch UK (EL HR), 60 Lightwood Rd, Buxton, Derbyshire SK17 (+44-1298-24300) (fax) (mail@genewatch.org) (www.genewatch.org). Monitors genetic engineering.

Global Justice Now (TW), 66 Offley Rd, London SW9 0LS (+44-20-7820 4900) (fax 7820 4949) (offleyroad@globaljustice.org.uk) (www.globaljustice.org.uk). *Ninety Nine.* Formerly World Development Movement.

Global Witness (EL HR TW CR), Lloyds Chambers, 1 Portsoken St, London E1 (+44-20-7492 5820) (fax 7492 5821) (mail@globalwitness.org) (www.globalwitness.org). Also in USA.

GM Freeze (EL), c/o 80 Cyprus St, Stretford, Manchester M32 (info@gmfreeze.org) (www.gmfreeze.org). Umbrella body.

GM Watch (EL), c/o 26 Pottergate, Norwich NR2 1DX, Norfolk (+44-1603-624021) (fax 766552) (ngin@gmwatch.org) (www.gmwatch.org). Analyses and counters GM industry propaganda.

GM-Free Cymru (EL), c/o Dyffryn Dwarch, Abermawr, nr Mathry, Pembrokeshire SA62 (gm@caerhys.co.uk) (www.gmfreecymru.co.uk).

GM-free Scotland (EL), c/o 35 Hamilton Drive, Glasgow G12 (gmfreescotland@yahoo.co.uk) (gmfreescotland.blogspot.co.uk).

Greater Manchester & District CND [GM&DCND] (ND), Bridge 5 Mill, 22a Beswick St, Ancoats, Manchester M4 7HR (+44-161-273 8283) (fax 273 8293) (gmdcnd@gn.apc.org) (www.gmdcnd.org.uk). *Nuclear Alert.*

Green Christian [GC] (EL PO), 97 Plumpton Ave, Hornchurch RM12 6BB, Essex (info@greenchristian.org.uk) (www.greenchristian.org.uk). *Green Christian.*

Green CND (ND), c/o CND, 162 Holloway Rd, London N7 (+44-20-7700 2393).

Green Party of England and Wales (EL ND HR RA), The Biscuit Factory - A Block (201), 100 Clements Rd, London SE16 4DG (+44-20-3691 9400) (office@greenparty.org.uk) (www.greenparty.org.uk). *Green World.*

GreenNet (TW HR PO), 56-64 Leonard St, London EC2 4LT (+44-20-7065 0935) (fax 7253 2658) (info@gn.apc.org) (www.gn.apc.org).

Greenpeace UK (GP), Canonbury Villas, London N1 2PN (+44-20-7865 8100) (fax 7865 8200) (info.uk@greenpeace.org) (www.greenpeace.org.uk). *Connect.*

Housmans Bookshop (WR EL AL HR), 5 Caledonian Rd, Kings Cross, London N1 9DX (+44-20-7837 4473) (fax 7278 0444) (shop@housmans.com) (www.housmans.com). *Peace Diary & World Peace Directory.* Peace/political books, magazines, cards, etc.

Human Rights Watch - London Office (HR), First Floor, Audrey House, 16-20 Ely Place, London EC1 (+44-20-7713 1995) (fax 7713 1800) (londonoutreach@hrw.org) (www.hrw.org/london/).

Humanists UK (HR PO), 39 Moreland St, London EC1V 8BB (+44-20-7324 3060) (fax 7324 3061) (info@humanists.uk) (humanism.org.uk). Formerly British Humanist Association.

Index on Censorship (HR RA TW), 292 Vauxhall Bridge Rd, London SW1V 1AE (+44-20-7963 7262) (david@indexoncensorship.org) (www.indexoncensorship.org). *Index on Censorship.*

Inter Faith Network for the UK (RP CR CD), 2 Grosvenor Gardens, London SW1W 0DH (+44-20-7730 0410) (fax 7730 0414) (ifnet@interfaith.org.uk) (www.interfaith.org.uk).

International Alert [IA] (RE CR HR CD), 346 Clapham Rd, London SW9 (+44-20-7627 6800) (fax 7627 6900) (general@international-alert.org) (www.international-alert.org).

International Association for Religious Freedom - British Chapter (HR), c/o Pejman Khojasteh, c/o Essex Hall, 1 Essex St, London WC2R 3HY (Pejman_Khojasteh@btinternet.com) (www.iarf.net). *IARF World.*

International Campaign to Abolish Nuclear Weapons - UK [ICAN-UK] (ND), c/o MEDACT, 28 Charles Sq, London N1 6HT (infouk@icanw.org) (www.icanw.org/unitedkingdom).

International Friendship League (British Section) (CD), PO Box 578, Northampton NN5 4WY (ifl.org.uk).

International Liberty Association (HR), Rowlandson House, 289-297 Ballards Lane, London N12 (+44-20-8906 7739) (info@iliberty.org.uk) (iliberty.org.uk). Formerly Iran Liberty Association.

International Service [UNAIS] (TW UN), Second Floor, Rougier House, 5 Rougier St, York YO1 6HZ (+44-1904-647799) (fax 652353) (contact@internationalservice.org.uk) (www.internationalservice.org.uk).

International Voluntary Service [IVS] (SC), Thorn House, 5 Rose St, Edinburgh EH2 2PR (+44-131-243 2745) (fax 243 2747) (info@ivsgb.org) (ivsgb.org). *Interactions.*

Iona Community (FR PA HR), 21 Carlton Court, Glasgow G5 9JP (+44-141-429 7281) (admin@iona.org.uk) (www.iona.org.uk). *The Coracle.* (On Iona: +44-1681-700404).

Israeli Committee Against House Demolitions UK [ICAHD UK] (HR RA), BM ICAHD UK, London WC1N 3XX (+44-20-3740 2208) (info@icahduk.org) (www.icahduk.org). Opposes Israeli occupation of Palestinian land.

JD Bernal Peace Library (RE), c/o Marx Memorial Library, 37a Clerkenwell Green, London EC1R 0DU (+44-20-7253 1485) (archives@mml.xyz) (www.marx-memorial-library.org). *Theory and Struggle.*

Jews for Justice for Palestinians [JfJfP] (HR), 20-22 Wenlock Rd, London N1 7GU (jfjfp@jfjfp.com) (jfjfp.com).

Jubilee Debt Campaign (TW), The Grayston Centre, 28 Charles Sq, London N1 6HT (+44-20-7324 4722) (fax 7324 4723) (info@jubileedebt.org.uk) (jubileedebt.org.uk). *Drop It!.*

Jubilee Scotland (TW), 41 George IV Bridge, Edinburgh EH1 1EL (+44-131-225 4321) (mail@jubileescotland.org.uk) (www.jubileescotland.org.uk). Successor to Jubilee 2000 Scottish Coalition.

Justice & Peace Scotland / Ceartas agus Sith (RP), 65 Bath St, Glasgow G2 2BX (+44-141-333 0238) (fax 331 2409) (office@justiceandpeacescotland.org.uk) (justiceandpeacescotland.org.uk).

Justice, Peace and Integrity of Creation project of the Columban Fathers [JPIC] (RP), St Joseph's, Waford Way, Hendon, London NW4 4TY (+44-20-8202 2555) (fax 8202 5775) (jpicssc@btconnect.com) (www.columbans.co.uk). *Vocation for Justice.*

Khulisa - Breaking the cycle of violence (CD CR PO), Wells House (Unit 7), 5-7 Wells Terrace, London N4 (+44-20-7561 3727) (info@khulisa.co.uk) (www.khulisa.co.uk). Modelled on programmes in South Africa.

Kick Nuclear (EL RA), c/o LRCND, 162 Holloway Rd, London N7 8DQ (+44-20-7607 2302) (kicknuclearlondon@gmail.com) (kicknuclear.com). Opposes UK's addiction to nuclear power.

Labour CND (ND), c/o 480 Lymingon Rd, Highcliffe, Christchurch BH23 5HG (+44-1425-279307) (info@labourcnd.org.uk) (www.labourcnd.org.uk).

Liberation (HR TW DA CR), 77 St John St, Clerkenwell, London EC1M 4NN (+44-20-7324 2498) (info@liberationorg.co.uk) (www.liberationorg.co.uk). *Liberation.*

Liberty - The National Council for Civil Liberties (HR), Liberty House, 26-30 Strutton Ground, London SW1P 2HR (+44-20-7403 3888) (fax 7799 5306) (www.liberty-human-rights.org.uk).

Living Streets (EL HR PO), 4th Floor, Universal House, 88-94 Wentworth St, London E1 7SA (+44-20-7377 4900) (info@livingstreets.org.uk) (www.livingstreets.org.uk).

Local Futures / ISEC [ISEC-UK] (EL), PO Box 239, Totnes TQ9 9DP (+44-1392-581175) (info@localfutures.org) (www.localfutures.org).

London Catholic Worker [LCW] (RP RA PA AL), 49 Mattison Rd, London N4 (+44-20-8348 8212) (londoncatholicworker@yahoo.co.uk) (www.londoncatholicworker.org). *London Catholic Worker.*

London Mining Network [LMN] (HR EL), Finfuture, 225-229 Seven Sisters Rd, London N4 (contact@londonminingnetwork.org) (www.londonminingnetwork.org).

London Region CND [LRCND] (ND), Mordechai Vannunu House, 162 Holloway Rd, London N7 8DQ (+44-20-7607 2302) (www.londoncnd.org.uk). *Peaceline.*

Low-Impact Living Initiative [LILI] (PO EL), Redfield Community, Winslow MK18, Bucks (+44-1296-714184) (fax) (lili@lowimpact.org) (www.lowimpact.org).

Low-Level Radiation Campaign [LLRC] (EL), Times Building, South Crescent, Llandrindod Wells, Powys LD1 5DH (+44-1597-824771) (lowradcampaign@gmail.com) (www.llrc.org).

MEDACT (IP IB EL), The Grayston Centre, 28 Charles Sq, London N1 6HT (+44-20-7324 4739) (fax 7324 4744) (office@medact.org) (www.medact.org). *Communiqué.*

Medical Aid for Palestinians [MAP] (HR), 33a Islington Park St, London N1 1QB (+44-20-7226 4114) (fax 7226 0880) (info@map-uk.org) (www.map-uk.org).

MENA Solidarity Network (HR), Unit 193, 15-17 Caledonian Rd, London N1 (menasolidarity@gmail.com) (www.menasolidaritynetwork.com).

Merseyside CND (ND), 151 Dale St, Liverpool L2 2AH (+44-151-229 5282) (mcnd@care4free.net) (www.mcnd.org.uk).

Methodist Peace Fellowship [MPF] (FR PA), c/o Marie Dove, 17 Fangdale Court, Bridlington, Yorks YO16 (+44-1262-679612) (marie.dove@gmail.com) (mpf.org.uk). *Peace in the 21st Century.*

Milton Keynes Peace & Justice Network (ND HR), 300 Saxon Gate West, Central Milton Keynes, Bucks MK9 2ES (+44-1908-561365) (office@mkpeaceandjustice.org.uk) (www.mkpeaceandjustice.org.uk). *MK Network News.*

Mines Advisory Group [MAG] (DA TW PO), Suite 3A, South Central, 11 Peter St, Manchester M2 5QR (+44-161-236 4311) (fax 236 6244) (info@maginternational.org) (www.maginternational.org).

Mothers Against Murder And Aggression [MAMAA UK], PO Box 778, Borehamwood WD6 9LF, Herts (+44-20-8207 0702) (info@mamaa.org) (www.mamaa.org).

Movement for Compassionate Living [MCL] (PO EL), 105 Cyfyng Rd, Ystalyfera, Swansea SA9 2BT (+44-1639-841223) (mcl.ystalyfera@googlemail.com) (www.MCLveganway.org.uk). *New Leaves.*

Movement for the Abolition of War [MAW] (IB), c/o 11 Venetia Rd, London N4 1EJ (+44-20-3397 3019) (info@abolishwar.org.uk) (www.abolishwar.org.uk). *Abolish War.*

Musicians for Peace and Disarmament [MPD] (IB NA DA), c/o Tony Lamb, 37 Bolton Gdns, Teddington TW11 9AX (info.mpdconcerts@gmail.com) (www.mpdconcerts.org). *Newsletter.*

National Federation of Atheist, Humanist and Secularist Student Societies [AHS] (HR), 39 Moreland St, London EC1 (communications@ahsstudents.org.uk) (ahsstudents.org.uk).

National Justice & Peace Network [NJPN] (RP), 39 Eccleston Sq, London SW1V 1BX (+44-20-7901 4864) (fax 7901 4821) (admin@justice-and-peace.org.uk) (www.justice-and-peace.org.uk). *Justice and Peace.*

National Secular Society [NSS] (HR), 25 Red Lion Sq, London WC1R 4RL (+44-20-7404 3126) (enquiries@secularism.org.uk) (www.secularism.org.uk).

Navigate: Facilitation for Social Change (RA AL CR EL), Old Music Hall, 106-108 Cowley Rd, Oxford OX4 (+44-1865-403134) (hello@navigate.org.uk) (www.navigate.org.uk). Formerly part of Seeds for Change network.

Network for Peace [NfP] (DA ND PA), 5 Caledonian Rd, London N1 9DX (mail@networkforpeace.org.uk) (www.networkforpeace.org.uk).

Network of Christian Peace Organisations [NCPO] (RP), c/o FOR, Peace House, 19 Paradise St, Oxford OX1 1LD (+44-1865-250781) (ncpo@for.org.uk) (ncpo.org.uk).

New Economics Foundation [NEF] (EL CD PO), 10 Salamanca Place, London SE1 7HB (+44-20-7820 6300) (info@neweconomics.org) (www.neweconomics.org).

Nicaragua Solidarity Campaign [NSC] (HR TW WC), 86 Durham Rd, London N7 7DT (+44-20-7561 4836) (nsc@nicaraguasc.org.uk) (www.nicaraguasc.org.uk). *Nicaragua Now.*

Nipponzan Myohoji (RP), Peace Pagoda, Willen, Milton Keynes MK15 0BA, Bucks (+44-1908-663652) (fax). Also in London: +44-20-7228 9620.

No 2 Nuclear Power (EL), c/o Pete Roche, Friends of the Earth Scotland, Thorn House, 5 Rose Street, Edinburgh EH2 (rochepete8@aol.com) (www.no2nuclearpower.org.uk). Provides new website and nuclear information.

No Sweat (HR RA TW), 5 Caledonian Rd, London N1 (admin@nosweat.org.uk) (www.nosweat.org.uk). Against sweatshops; for workers' and TU rights.

NO2ID (HR), Box 412, 19-21 Crawford St, London W1H 1PJ (+44-20-7340 6077) (office@no2id.net) (www.no2id.net). *NO2ID Newsletter.* Opposes ID cards and the database state.

Non-Violent Resistance Network [NVRN] (RA ND PA), c/o David Polden, CND, 162 Holloway Rd, London N7 8DQ (+44-20-7607 2302) (david.lrcnd@cnduk.org). *Newsletter.*

Northern Friends Peace Board [NFPB] (SF), Victoria Hall, Knowsley St, Bolton BL1 2AS (+44-1204-382330) (nfpb@gn.apc.org) (nfpb.org.uk). *The Peace Board.*

Norwich Environment Resource Centre (EL PO), The Greenhouse, 42-46 Bethel St, Norwich NR2 1NR (+44-1603-631007) (www.GreenhouseTrust.co.uk).

Nuclear Awareness Group [NAG] (EL), 16 Back St, Winchester SO23 9SB, Hants (+44-1962-890160) (fax) (nuclearawarenessgroup.org.uk). *Newsletter.*

Nuclear Information Service [NIS] (RE ND), 35-39 London St, Reading RG1 4PS (+44-118-327 4935) (office@nuclearinfo.org) (nuclearinfo.org).

Nuclear Morality Flowchart Project (ND), c/o Martin Birdseye, 88 Fern Lane, Hounslow TW5 0HJ, Middlesex (+44-20-8571 1691) (info@nuclearmorality.com) (nuclearmorality.com). Helps people to think about ethical accountability.

Nuclear Trains Action Group [NTAG] (ND RA), c/o Mordechai Vanunu House, 162 Holloway Rd, London N7 8DR (+44-20-7607 2302) (david.lrcnd@cnduk.org) (www.nonucleartrains.org.uk). *Newletter.* Working Group of London Region CND.

BRITAIN

Nuclear-Free Local Authorities Secretariat [NFLA] (ND EL), c/o Manchester City Council, Town Hall, Manchester M60 3NY (+44-161-234 3244) (fax 274 7379) (s.morris4@manchester.gov.uk) (www.nuclearpolicy.info).

Nukewatch UK (ND RA), c/o Edinburgh Peace & Justice Centre, 5 Upper Bow, Edinburgh EH1 2JN (+44-345 458 8364) (spotters@nukewatch.org.uk) (www.nukewatch.org.uk).

Oasis of Peace UK (CD CR HR), 192B Station Rd, Edgware HA8 7AR, Middx (+44-20-8952 4717) (office@oasisofpeace.org.uk) (www.oasisofpeaceuk.org.uk). Formerly British Friends of NSWaS.

One World Week (HR TW EL), 35-39 London St, Reading RG1 4PS, Berks (+44-118-939 4933) (oww@oneworldweek.org) (www.oneworldweek.org).

OneVoice Movement - Europe (CD CR), Unit 4, Benwell Studios, 11-13 Benwell Rd, London N7 7BL (+44-20-8004 6431) (europe@OneVoiceMovement.org) (www.onevoicemovement.org). See also under Israel, Palestine, and USA.

Orthodox Peace Fellowship UK [OPF] (RP), c/o Seraphim Honeywell, "Birchenhoe", Crowfield, nr Brackley NN13 5TW, Northants (oxpeacefp@aol.com) (www.incommunion.org). *In Communion.*

Oxford Research Group (RE CR DA), Development House, 56-64 Leonard St, London EC2A 4LT (+44-20-7549 0298) (org@oxfordresearchgroup.org.uk) (www.oxfordresearchgroup.org.uk).

Palestine Solidarity Campaign [PSC] (TW CR), Box BM PSA, London WC1N 3XX (+44-20-7700 6192) (fax 7700 5747) (info@palestinecampaign.org) (www.palestinecampaign.org).

Pax Christi (PC PA RE), Christian Peace Education Centre, St Joseph's, Watford Way, Hendon, London NW4 4TY (+44-20-8203 4884) (fax 8203 5234) (info@paxchristi.org.uk) (www.paxchristi.org.uk). *Justpeace.*

Peace Brigades International - UK Section [PBI UK] (PA RE HR CD), 1b Waterlow Rd, London N19 5NJ (+44-20-7281 5370) (fax) (admin@peacebrigades.org.uk) (www.peacebrigades.org.uk).

Peace Direct (CR RE), Studio 302, 203-213 Mare St, London E8 (+44-20-3422 5549) (info@peacedirect.org) (www.peacedirect.org).

Peace Education Network (RE), c/o Pax Christi, St Joseph's, Watford Way, London NW4 4TY (+44-20-8203 4884) (education@paxchristi.org.uk) (www.peace-education.org.uk).

Peace in Kurdistan (HR), 44 Ainger Rd, London NW3 3AT (+44-20-7586 5892) (estella24@tiscali.co.uk) (www.peaceinkurdistancampaign.com).

Peace Museum UK (RE PA CR), 10 Piece Hall Yard, off Hustlergate, Bradford BD1 1PJ (+44-1274-780241) (info@peacemuseum.org.uk) (www.peacemuseum.org.uk).

***Peace News - for nonviolent revolution* [PN]** (WR HR AL PA RND), 5 Caledonian Rd, London N1 9DY (+44-20-7278 3344) (fax 7278 0444) (editorial@peacenews.info) (www.peacenews.info).

Peace One Day (CR PO RE), St George's House, 15 St George's Rd, Richmond, Surrey TW9 (+44-20-8334 9900) (fax 8948 0545) (info@peaceoneday.org) (www.peaceoneday.org).

Peace Party - Non-violence, Justice, Environment (PA HR EL), c/o John Morris, 39 Sheepfold Rd, Guildford GU2 9TT, Surrey (+44-1483-576400) (info@peaceparty.org.uk) (www.peaceparty.org.uk). *Peace.* Secular pacifist electoral movement.

Peace Pledge Union [PPU] (WR RE), 1 Peace Passage, Brecknock Rd, London N7 0BT (+44-20-7424 9444) (mail@ppu.org.uk) (www.ppu.org.uk). *Peace Matters.*

Peace Tax Seven (TR), c/o Woodlands, Ledge Hill, Market Lavington, Wilts SN10 (info@peacetaxseven.com) (www.peacetaxseven.com).

People & Planet (TW HR EL), The Old Music Hall, 106-108 Cowley Rd, Oxford OX4 1JE (+44-1865-403225) (people@peopleandplanet.org) (peopleandplanet.org). National student network.

People Against Rio Tinto and its Subsidiaries [PARTIZANS] (HR EL TW), 41A Thornhill Sq, London N1 1BE (+44-20-7700 6189) (fax) (partizans@gn.apc.org) (www.minesandcommunities.org).

Practical Action (PO TW), Schumacher Centre for Technology and Development, Bourton Hall, Bourton-on-Dunsmore, Rugby, Warwickshire CV23 9QZ (+44-1926-634400) (fax 634401) (enquiries@practicalaction.org.uk) (www.practicalaction.org).

Pugwash Conferences on Science and World Affairs (DA EL RE TW CR), Ground Floor Flat, 63A Great Russell St, London WC1B 3BJ (+44-20-7405 6661) (office@britishpugwash.org) (britishpugwash.org). *Pugwash Newsletter.* Part of international Pugwash network.

Quaker Concern for the Abolition of Torture [Q-CAT] (SF HR), c/o 38 The Mount, Heswall CH60 4RA, Wirral (+44-151-342 4425) (chasraws@onetel.com) (q-cat.org.uk).

Quaker Peace & Social Witness [QPSW] (SF DA PA), Friends House, 175 Euston Rd, London NW1 2BJ (+44-20-7663 1000) (qpsw@quaker.org.uk) (www.quaker.org.uk/qpsw).

Quaker Sustainability and Peace Programme (SF EL RE DA PA), QPSW, Friends House, 175 Euston Rd, London NW1 2BJ (+44-20-7663 1067) (fax 7663 1001) (survival@quaker.org.uk) (www.quaker.org.uk). Previously Peace and Disarmament Programme.

Radical Routes (AL PO), c/o Cornerstone Resource Centre, 16 Sholebroke Ave, Leeds LS7 3HB (enquiries@radicalroutes.org.uk) (www.radicalroutes.org.uk). Network of radical housing, worker & other co-ops.

Redress (HR), 87 Vauxhall Walk, London SE11 (+44-20-7793 1777) (fax 7793 1719) (info@redress.org) (www.redress.org). Seeks justice for torture survivors.

Religions for Peace [WCRP-UK] (RP RE), c/o 18 Little Acres, Ware SG12 9JW, Hertfordshire (+44-1920-465714) (fax) (secretary@religionsforpeace.org.uk) (www.religionsforpeace.org.uk).

Religious Society of Friends in Britain (Quakers) (SF), Friends House, Euston Rd, London NW1 2BJ (+44-20-7663 1000) (fax 7663 1001) (www.quaker.org.uk). *Quaker News; The Friend; Quaker Voices.*

Remote Control Project (DA RE), c/o Oxford Research Group, Development House, 56-64 Leonard St, London EC2A 4LT (+44-20-7549 0298) (remotecontrolproject.org). Challenges "behind the scenes" warfare.

Reprieve (HR), PO Box 72054, London EC3P 3BZ (+44-20-7553 8140) (info@reprieve.org.uk) (www.reprieve.org.uk).

Responding to Conflict [RTC] (CR RE), 1046 Bristol Rd, Selly Oak, Birmingham B29 6LJ (+44-121-415 5641) (fax 415 4119) (enquiries@respond.org) (www.respond.org). Training and resources.

Rising Tide UK [RTUK] (EL RA AL), c/o London Action Resource Centre, 62 Fieldgate St, Whitechapel, London E1 1ES (info@risingtide.org.uk) (www.risingtide.org.uk). Direct action for climate justice.

RoadPeace (EL RE HR), Shakespeare Business Centre, 245a Coldharbour Lane, London SW9 8RR (+44-20-7733 1603) (info@roadpeace.org) (roadpeace.org). Supports traffic victims and families.

Saferworld (RE AT), The Grayston Centre, 28 Charles Sq, London N1 (+44-20-7324 4646) (fax 7324 4647) (general@saferworld.org.uk) (www.saferworld.org.uk). Helping people turn away from armed violence.

Scientists for Global Responsibility [SGR] (RE ND EL AT DA), Unit 2.8, Halton Mill, Mill Lane, Halton, Lancaster LA2 6ND, Lancashire (+44-1524-812073) (info@sgr.org.uk) (www.sgr.org.uk). *SGR Newsletter.*

Scotland's for Peace (ND RE AT), c/o 77 Southpark Ave, Glasgow G12 (+44-141-357 1529) (info@scotland4peace.org) (www.scotland4peace.org). Umbrella body.

Scottish Campaign for Nuclear Disarmament [SCND] (ND), 77 Southpark Ave, Glasgow G12 8LE (+44-141-357 1529) (scnd@banthebomb.org) (www.banthebomb.org). *Nuclear Free Scotland.*

Scottish Friends of Palestine (HR TW), 31 Tinto Rd, Glasgow G43 2AL (+44-141-637 8046) (info@scottish-friends-of-palestine.org) (www.scottishfriendsofpalestine.org).

Scottish Green Party (EL), Bonnington Mill, 72 Newhaven Rd, Edinburgh EH6 5QG (greens.scot).

Scrap Trident Coalition (ND PA RA), c/o Edinburgh Peace and Justice Centre, 5 Upper Bow, Edinburgh EH1 2JN (+44-131-629 1058) (scraptrident@gmail.com) (scraptrident.org). Network in Scotland.

Sea Shepherd UK (EL RA), 27 Old Gloucester St, London WC1N 3AX (+44-300-111 0501) (admin@seashepherduk.org) (www.seashepherd.org.uk). Conserving nature on the high seas.

SEAD - Scottish Education and Action for Development (PO RA TW), Norton Park, 57 Albion Rd, Edinburgh EH7 (+44-131-475 2612) (info@sead.org.uk) (www.sead.org.uk).

Seeds for Change (RA AL), Storey Institute, Meeting House Lane, Lancaster LA1 (+44-1524-509002) (contact@seedsforchange.org.uk) (www.seedsforchange.org.uk). Training for actions, campaigns, setting up co-ops.

Servas Britain (SE), c/o Nash Villa, Nash Lane, Marnhull, Sturminster Newton DT10, Dorset (info@servasbritain.net) (www.servasbritain.net).

Share The World's Resources [STWR] (TW EL), PO Box 52662, London N7 8UX (+44-20-7609 3034) (info@sharing.org) (www.sharing.org). Sustainable economics to end global poverty.

Smash EDO (RA AT), c/o Unemployed Centre, 6 Tilbury Place, Brighton BN2 0GY, Sussex (smashedo@riseup.net) (smashedo.org.uk).

Soil Association (EL PO TW), South Plaza, Marlborough St, Bristol BS1 (+44-117-314 5000) (fax 314 5001) (memb@soilassociation.org) (www.soilassociation.org). Scotland office: +44-131-666 2474.

South Cheshire & North Staffs CND [SCANS CND] (ND), Groundwork Enterprise Centre, Albany Works, Moorland Rd, Burslem, Stoke-on-Trent ST6 1EB, Staffs (+44-1782-829913) (scanscnd@ymail.com) (www.scanscnd.org.uk). *Banner.*

Southdowns Peace Group (DA), c/o Vida, 22 Beaufort Rd, Bedhampton, Havant PO9 3HU (+44-23-9234 6696) (vida.henning@ntlworld.com).

Southern Region CND (ND), 3 Harpsichord Place, Oxford OX4 1BY (+44-1865-248357) (oxfordcnd@phonecoop.coop).

St Ethelburga's Centre for Reconciliation and Peace (CD CR RE RP), 78 Bishopsgate, London EC2N 4AG (+44-20-7496 1610) (fax 7638 1440) (enquiries@stethelburgas.org) (www.stethelburgas.org).

Stop Arming Israel (AT), c/o CAAT, Unit 4, 5-7 Wells Terrace, London N4 3JU (+44-20-7281 0297) (israel@caat.org.uk) (www.stoparmingisrael.org). Joint campaign of peace, solidarity, etc, groups.

Stop Climate Chaos Scotland [SCCS] (EL), 2nd Floor, Thorn House, 5 Rose St, Edinburgh EH2 2PR (+44-131-243 2701) (info@stopclimatechaosscotland.org) (www.stopclimatechaos.org/scotland). Development, environment, etc, groups' coalition.

Stop Hinkley (EL), 8 The Bartons, Yeabridge, South Petherton TA13 5LW, Somerset (+44-1749-860767) (admin@stophinkley.org) (www.stophinkley.org). Against nuclear power in south-west England.

Stop the War Coalition [STWC], 86 Durham Rd, London N7 (+44-20-7561 4830) (office@stopwar.org.uk) (www.stopwar.org.uk).

Student Christian Movement [SCM] (RP), Grays Court, 3 Nursery Rd, Edgbaston, Birmingham B15 3JX (+44-121-426 4918) (scm@movement.org.uk) (www.movement.org.uk).

Surfers Against Sewage [SAS] (EL), Unit 2, Wheal Kitty Workshops, St Agnes TR5 0RD, Cornwall (+44-1872-553001) (fax 552615) (info@sas.org.uk) (www.sas.org.uk). *Pipeline News.*

Sustain: The Alliance for Better Food and Farming (EL PO), Development House, 56-64 Leonard St, London EC2 (+44-20-7065 0902) (sustain@sustainweb.org) (www.sustainweb.org).

Syria Peace & Justice Group (CR CD AT DA), c/o LARC, 62 Fieldgate St, London E1 (syriapeaceandjustice@gmail.com) (syriapeaceandjustice.wordpress.com). Anti-militarist human rights campaign.

Syrian Human Rights Committee [SHRC] (HR), PO Box 123, Edgware HA8 0XF, Middlesex (fax +44-870-1377678) (walid@shrc.org) (www.shrc.org). Syrian human rights group in exile.

Tapol (HR AT TW RE), Durham Resource Centre, 86 Durham Rd, London N7 (+44-20-7561 7485) (info@tapol.org) (www.tapol.org).

The Brotherhood Church (PA AL EL), Stapleton, nr Pontefract, Yorkshire WF8 3DF (+44-1977-620381).

The Climate Coalition (EL), c/o Oxfam, 3rd Floor North, Victoria Charity Centre, 11 Belgrave Rd, London SW1 (+44-20-7802 9989) (admin@theclimatecoalition.org) (www.theclimatecoalition.org).

The Corner House (HR TW EL), Station Rd, Sturminster Newton, Dorset DT10 1BB (+44-1258-473795) (fax) (enquiries@thecornerhouse.org.uk) (www.thecornerhouse.org.uk). *Briefing Papers.*

The Forgiveness Project (CR PO), 42a Buckingham Palace Rd, London SW1 (+44-20-7821 0035) (info@theforgivenessproject.com) (www.theforgivenessproject.com).

The Land Magazine (EL RA), c/o Monkton Wyld Court, Charmouth, Bridport, Dorset DT6 (+44-1297-561359) (editorial@thelandmagazine.org.uk) (www.thelandmagazine.org.uk). occl. Land rights campaign.

"The Right to Refuse to Kill" Group [RRK] (PA HR), c/o PPU, 1 Peace Passage, London N7 0BT (+44-20-7237 3731) (edna.mathieson1@btinternet.com) (www.rrk.freeuk.com).

Think Global - the Development Education Association (TW), CAN Mezzanine, 32-36 Loman St, London SE1 (+44-20-3751 3000) (info@think-global.org) (think-global.org.uk).

Tibet Foundation (HR), Room 304, 5 Westminster Bridge Rd, London SE1 (+44-20-7930 6001) (info@tibet-foundation.org) (www.tibet-foundation.org).

Tibet Society (HR TW CR), 2 Baltic Place, London N1 5AQ (+44-20-7923 0021) (info@tibetsociety.com) (www.tibetsociety.com). Campaigns for Tibetan self-determination.

Tolerance International - UK (CR HR RE), Scandinavian House, 2-6 Cannon St, London EC4 (+44-20-7097 5167) (fax) (tolernace@toleranceinternational.org.uk) (www.toleranceinternational.org.uk).

Tools for Self Reliance (TW PO WC), Ringwood Rd, Netley Marsh, Southampton SO40 7GY (+44-23-8086 9697) (fax 8086 8544) (info@tfsr.org) (www.tfsr.org). *Forging Links.*

Tourism Concern (TW HR EL), The Lansdowne Building, 2 Lansdowne Rd, Croydon CR9 (+44-20-8263 6007) (fax 8263 6001) (info@tourismconcern.org.uk) (www.tourismconcern.org.uk).

Town and Country Planning Association [TCPA] (EL), 17 Carlton House Terr, London SW1Y 5AS (+44-20-7930 8903) (fax 7930 3280) (tcpa@tcpa.org.uk) (www.tcpa.org.uk). *Town & Country Planning.*

Trade Justice Movement (TW HR EL), c/o Fairtrade Foundation, 3rd Floor, Ibex House, 42-47 Minories, London EC3N 1DY (+44-20-7440 8560) (mail@tjm.org.uk) (www.tjm.org.uk).

Trident Ploughshares (WR ND RA), c/o Edinburgh Peace & Justice Centre, 5 Upper Bow, Edinburgh EH1 2JN (+44-345 458 8361) (tp2000@gn.apc.org) (tridentploughshares.org).

Turning the Tide (SF PO RA), Friends House, Euston Rd, London NW1 2BJ (+44-20-7663 1064) (fax 7663 1049) (stevew@quaker.org.uk) (www.turning-the-tide.org). *Making Waves.* Offers workshops, nonviolence training, etc.

Tyne & Wear CND (ND), 1 Rectory Ave, Gosforth, Newcastle-upon-Tyne NE3 1XS (+44-191-285 1290) (rhpg@btinternet.com).

UK Committee for UNICEF [UNICEF UK] (TW HR), UNICEF House, 30a Great Sutton St, London EC1 (+44-20-7490 2388) (fax 7250 1733) (www.unicef.org.uk).

UK WILPF - Scottish Office (WL), 4 Hunter Sq, Edinburgh EH1 1QW (scottishwilpf@yahoo.co.uk) (www.wilpf.org). Main office in London (+44-20-7250 1968).

UNA Exchange (UN WC PO), Temple of Peace, Cathays Park, Cardiff CF10 3AP (+44-29-2022 3088) (fax 2022 2540) (info@unaexchange.org) (www.unaexchange.org). *Opinions.*

UNA-UK Members for Civil Society Link with UN General Assembly [UNGA-Link UK] (UN), 11 Wilberforce House, 119 Worple Rd, London SW20 8ET (+44-20-8944 0574) (fax) (info@ungalink.org.uk) (www.ungalink.org.uk).

Unitarian and Free Christian Peace Fellowship [UPF] (RP), c/o Sue Woolley, 5 Martins Rd, Piddinston, Northampton NN7 2DN (+44-1455-636602) (www.unitariansocieties.org.uk/peace).

United Nations Association - UK [UNA-UK] (UN HR RE TW), 3 Whitehall Court, London SW1A 2EL (+44-20-7766 3454) (fax 7000 1381) (info@una.org.uk) (www.una.org.uk). *UNA-UK.*

United Nations Association - Wales [UNA/CCU] (UN WF), Temple of Peace and Health / Y Deml Heddwch, Cathays Park, Cardiff CF10 3AP (+44-29-2022 8549) (fax 2064 0333) (una@wcia.org.uk) (www.wcia.org.uk/una). *Newsletter.*

United Reformed Church Peace Fellowship [URCPF] (RP), c/o Church and Society, United Reformed Church, 86 Tavistock Pl, London WC1H 9RT (+44-20-7916 8632) (fax 7916 2021) (church.society@urc.org.uk) (www.urc.org.uk/mission/peace-fellowship.html).

Uniting for Peace [UfP] (DA ND CD AT RE), 14 Cavell St, London E1 2HP (+44-20-7791 1717) (info@unitingforpeace.com) (unitingforpeace.com). *Uniting for Peace.* Also in Edinburgh (+44-131-446 9545).

Vegan Society (EL TW PO HR), Donald Watson House, 21 Hylton St, Hockley, Birmingham B18 6HJ (+44-121-523 1730) (info@vegansociety.com) (www.vegansociety.com). *The Vegan.*

Vegetarian Society of the UK (EL TW PO), Parkdale, Dunham Rd, Altrincham, Cheshire (+44-161-925 2000) (fax 926 9182) (info@vegsoc.org) (www.vegsoc.org). *The Vegetarian.*

Veggies (PO EL), c/o Sumac Centre, 245 Gladstone St, Nottingham NG7 (+44-115-960 8254) (info@veggies.org.uk) (www.veggies.org.uk).

Veterans for Peace UK [VFP UK] (PA RA RE), 12 Dixon Rd, London SE25 6TZ (coord@vfpuk.org) (veteransforpeace.org.uk).

Voices for Creative Non-Violence UK [VCNV-UK] (PA CR), 31 Carisbrooke Rd, St Leonards-on-Sea TN38 0JN, Sussex (vcnvuk@gmail.com) (www.vcnv.org.uk).

Voluntary Service Overseas [VSO] (TW), 100 London Rd, Kingston-upon-Thames KT2, Surrey (+44-20-8780 7500) (enquiry@vsoint.org) (www.vsointernational.org).

Volunteer Action for Peace [VAP UK] (WC HR EL), 16 Overhill Rd, East Dulwich, London SE22 0PH (action@vap.org.uk) (www.vap.org.uk). Within UK, tel 0844-209 0927.

Volunteering Matters (PO CD), The Levy Centre, 18-24 Lower Clapton Rd, London E5 (+44-20-3780 5870) (information@volunteeringmatters.org.uk) (volunteeringmatters.org.uk). Formerly Community Service Volunteers.

War Child (RE PA PO), Linton House, 39-51 Highgate Rd, London NW5 1RT (+44-20-7916 9276) (info@warchild.org.uk) (www.warchild.org.uk). Aid organisation for children in war zones.

War On Want [WOW] (TW), 44-48 Shepherdess Walk, London N1 7JP (+44-20-7324 5040) (fax 7324 5041) (support@waronwant.org) (www.waronwant.org).

Week of Prayer for World Peace (RP), c/o 126 Manor Green Rd, Epsom KT19 8LN, Surrey (+44-1628-530309) (j.jackson215@btinternet.com) (www.weekofprayerforworldpeace.com).

Welsh Alliance Against Nuclear Weapons (ND), c/o George Crabb, 1 Woodstock House, 83 High St, Cowbridge CF71 7AF (+44-1446-774452) (georgecrabb@ybontfaen.freeserve.co.uk).

BRITAIN

West Midlands CND [WMCND] (ND), 54 Allison St, Digbeth, Birmingham B5 5TH (+44-121-643 4617) (wmcndall@gmail.com) (www.wmcnd.org).

West Midlands Quaker Peace Education Project [WMQPEP] (SF RE CR), 41 Bull St, Birmingham B4 6AF (+44-121-236 4796) (office@peacemakers.org.uk) (www.peacemakers.org.uk).

Western Sahara Campaign UK (HR TW), Manora, Cwmystwyth, Aberystwyth SY23 4AF (+44-1974-282575) (coordinator@wsahara.org.uk) (www.wsahara.org.uk).

White Ribbon Campaign (PO), White Ribbon House, 1 New Rd, Mytholmroyd, Hebden Bridge HX7 5DZ (+44-1422-886545) (info@whiteribboncampaign.co.uk) (www.whiteribboncampaign.co.uk).

WMD Awareness Programme (RE DA), c/o Pugwash Office, Bell Push 13, 63A Great Russell St, London WC1B 3BJ (+44-20-7405 6661) (office@wmdawareness.org.uk) (www.wmdawareness.org.uk).

Women for Women International - UK Office (HR TW), 32-36 Loman St, London SE1 0EH (+44-20-7922 7765) (fax 7922 7706) (supportuk@womenforwomen.org) (www.womenforwomen.org.uk). Aid, support, training for women in war zones.

Women in Black, c/o 24 Colvestone Cres, London E8 (wibinfo@gn.apc.org) (www.womeninblack.org.uk).

Women's International League for Peace and Freedom [UK WILPF] (WL), 52-54 Featherstone St, London EC1Y 8RT (+44-20-7250 1968) (ukwilpf.peace@gmail.com) (www.wilpf.org.uk). Also Scottish office (scottishwilpf@yahoo.co.uk).

Woodcraft Folk (PA EL PO RE TW), Units 9/10, 83 Crampton St, London SE17 (+44-20-7703 4173) (fax 7358 6370) (info@woodcraft.org.uk) (www.woodcraft.org.uk). *The Courier*. Co-operative children's and youth organisation.

Working Group on Conscientious Objection in the UK (HR), c/o ForcesWatch, 5 Caledonian Rd, London N1 (office@forceswatch.net). Network of pacifist and human rights groups.

World Future Council - UK Office (WF EL DA ND), 100 Pall Mall, St James', London SW1Y 5NQ (+44-20-7321 3810) (fax 7321 3738) (info.uk@worldfuturecouncil.org) (www.worldfuturecouncil.org). Promotes sustainable future.

World Peace Campaign, Hill House, Cookley, Kidderminster DY10 3UW, Worcs (+44-1562-851101) (fax 851824) (office@worldpeacecampaign.co.uk) (www.worldpeacecampaign.co.uk).

World Peace Prayer Society [WPPS] (RP PO EL RE), Allanton Sanctuary, Auldgirth, Dumfries DG2 0RY (+44-1387-740642) (allanton@worldpeace-uk.org) (www.worldpeace-uk.org). Promote the message "May peace prevail on earth".

Yorkshire CND (ND), 2 Ashgrove, Bradford BD7 1BN, West Yorks (+44-1274-730795) (info@yorkshirecnd.org.uk) (www.yorkshirecnd.org.uk). *Action for Peace*.

Youth and Student CND [YSCND] (ND RA), 162 Holloway Rd, London N7 8DQ (+44-20-7700 2393) (yscnd@riseup.net) (www.yscnd.org).

BULGARIA

Zelenitye / The Greens (EL HR ND), PK 1554, 1000 Sofiya (info@zelenite.bg) (izbori.zelenite.bg).
One of 2 Green Parties in Bulgaria.

BURMA

Peace for Burma Coalition [PFB] (HR), see under Thailand. Coalition of Burmese and Thai civil society groups.

Peace Way Foundation (HR), see under Thailand.

BURUNDI

Shalom - Educating for Peace (RE), Bujumbura (for postal address see Rwanda office) (hareprime@yahoo.fr).

CAMBODIA

Centre for Peace and Conflict Studies (RE), PO Box 93066, Siem Reap City (info@centrepeace.asia) (www.centrepeaceconflictstudies.org).

Youth for Peace Cambodia, 4-6G - St 513 - Sangat Beung Kok1, Khan Tuol Kok, Phnom Penh (+855-23-881346) (fax) (admin@yfpcambodia.org) (www.yfpcambodia.org).

CAMEROON

Research Centre for Peace, Human Rights and Rural Development [REPERID] (RE HR TW), PO Box 4131, Ghana Street - Nkwen, Bamenda, North West Region (+237-3336 3070) (info@reperid.org) (www.reperid.org).

CANADA

ACT for the Earth (WR IB AL), PO Box 52007, Oakville, ON, L6J 7N5 (+1-905-849 5501) (info@actfortheearth.org) (www.actfortheearth.org). *The ACTivist*.

Action by Christians Against Torture / Action des Chrétiens pour l'Abolition de la torture [ACAT-Canada] (HR), 2715 chemin de la Côte-Ste-Catherine, Montréal, QC, H3T 1B6 (+1-514-890 6169) (fax 890 6484) (info@acatcanada.org) (www.acatcanada.org).

Alternatives to Violence Project [AVP Canada] (CR), PO Box 157, Hastings, ON, K0L 1Y0 (schroeder.avp@sympatico.ca) (avpcanada.webs.com).

Amnesty International Canadian Section - English Speaking (AI), 312 Laurier Ave E, Ottawa, ON, K1N 1H9 (+1-613-744 7667) (fax 746 2411) (members@amnesty.ca) (www.amnesty.ca). *The Activist.*

Amnistie Internationale - Section Canadienne Francophone (AI), 50 rue Ste-Catherine Ouest - bureau 500, Montréal, QC, H2X 3V4 (+1-514-766 9766) (fax 766 2088) (www.amnistie.qc.ca).

Antennes de Paix - Montréal (PC), 2450 chemin de la Cote Sainte-Catherine - bureau 310, Montréal, Québec H3T 1B1 (+1-514-271 9198) (antennesdepaix@gmail.com) (antennesdepaixmontreal.blogspot.com).

Baptist Peace Fellowship of North America - Bautistas por la Paz (RP), see under USA.

Canadian Association of Physicians for the Environment (EL), 301-130 Spadina Ave, Toronto, ON, M5V 2L4 (+1-416-306 2273) (fax 960 9392) (cape.ca).

Canadian Coalition for Nuclear Responsibility [CCNR] (ND EL CD), 53 Dufferin Rd, Hampstead, QC, H3X 2X8 (+1-514-489 5118) (ccnr@web.net) (www.ccnr.org).

Canadian Friends Service Committee / Secours Quaker Canadien (SF), 60 Lowther Av, Toronto, ON, M5R 1C7 (+1-416-920 5213) (fax 920 5214) (info@quakerservice.ca) (www.quakerservice.ca). *Quaker Concern.*

Canadian Network to Abolish Nuclear Weapons [CNANW] (ND), 30 Cleary Ave, Ottawa, ON, K2A 4A1 (+1-613-233 1982) (fax 233 9028) (web.net/~cnanw).

Canadian Peace Congress (WP), 125 Brandon Ave, Toronto, ON, M6H 2E2 (info@CanadianPeaceCongress.ca) (www.canadianpeacecongress.ca).

Christian Peacemaker Teams [CPT Canada] (RP PA RA), 140 Westmnount Rd N, Waterloo, ON, N2L 3G6 (+1-416-423 5525) (canada@cpt.org) (www.cpt.org).

Civilian Peace Service Canada (CD PO), 2106-1025 Richmond Rd, Ottawa, ON, K2B 8G8 (+1-613-721 9829) (gbreedyk@civilianpeaceservice.org) (civilianpeaceservice.ca).

Coalition for Gun Control, PO Box 90062, 1488 Queen St West, Toronto, ON, M6K 3K3 (+1-416-604 0209) (coalitionforguncontrol@gmail.com) (guncontrol.ca). Also in Montreal (+1-514-528 2360).

Coalition to Oppose the Arms Trade [COAT] (AT), 191 James St, Ottawa, ON, K1R 5M6 (+1-613-231 3076) (overcoat@rogers.com) (coat.ncf.ca).

Daughters for Life (CR PO HR), 158 Pearl St - Suite 200, Toronto, ON, M5H 1L3 (+1-416-640 0246) (info@daughtersforlife.com) (www.daughtersforlife.com). Supports education of young women in Middle East.

Edmonton Peace Council (WP), 392 Meadowview Drive, Fort Saskatchewan, Alberta T8L 0N9 (+1-587-873 9739) (canadianpeace@gmail.com). *Alberta Peace News.*

Friends of the Earth / Les Ami(e)s de la Terre [FoE] (FE), 260 St Patrick St - Suite 300, Ottawa, ON, K1N 5K5 (+1-613-241 0085) (fax 241 7998) (foe@intranet.ca) (www.foecanada.org).

Greenpeace Canada (GP), 33 Cecil St, Toronto, ON, M5T 1N1 (+1-416-597 8408) (fax 597 8422) (supporter.ca@greenpeace.org) (www.greenpeace.ca).

Mines Action Canada / Action Mines Canada (AT HR DA), 86A Renfrew Ave, Ottawa, ON, K1S 1Z8 (+1-613-241 3777) (fax 244 3410) (info@minesactioncanada.org) (www.minesactioncanada.org).

Pace e Bene Canada (PA RP), 4058 Rivard, Montreal, Quebec, H2L 4H9 (veronow@sympatico.ca).

Peace Brigades International - Canada [PBI-Canada] (CR RE SD), 145 Spruce St - Suite 206, Ottawa, ON, K1R 6P1 (+1-613-237 6968) (fax 563 0017) (info@pbicanada.org) (www.pbicanada.org). *Newsletter.*

Peace Magazine (PA AT CR), Box 248, Toronto P, Toronto, ON, M5S 2S7 (+1-416-789 2294) (office@peacemagazine.org) (www.peacemagazine.org). 4 yrly, Can$20 (Can$24 US, Can$35 elsewhere).

Physicians for Global Survival (Canada) / Médecins pour la Survie Mondiale (Canada) [PGS] (IP IB), 30 Cleary Ave, Ottawa, ON, K2A 4A1 (+1-613-233 1982) (pgsadmin@web.ca) (pgs.ca).

Project Ploughshares (RE AT ND RP DA), 140 Westmount Rd North, Waterloo, ON, N2L 3G6 (+1-519-888 6541) (fax 888 0018) (plough@ploughshares.ca) (www.ploughshares.ca).

Réseau de Recherche sur les Opérations de Paix [ROP] (RE), Université de Montréal, Pavillion 3744 Jean-Brillant, Cerium, CP 6128, Succ Centre-ville, QC, H3C 3J7 (+1-514-343 7536) (www.operationspaix.net).

Religions for Peace - Canada / Religions pour la Paix - Canada (RP RE PA), 3333 Queen Mary Rd 490-1, Montréal, QC, H3Z 1A2 (pascale.fremond@videotron.ca).

Science for Peace [SfP] (RE ND), 045 University College, 15 King's College Circle, Toronto, ON, M5S 3H7 (+1-416-978 3606) (sfp@utoronto.ca) (scienceforpeace.sa.utoronto.ca).

Toronto Action for Social Change / Homes not Bombs [TASC] (RA AL), PO Box 2020, 57 Foster St, Perth, ON, K7H 1R0 (+1-613-267 3998) (tasc@web.ca) (www.homesnotbombs.blogspot.ca). *Resources for Radicals.*

CANADA

Trudeau Centre for Peace, Conflict and Justice (RE), Monk School of Global Affairs, University of Toronto, 1 Devonshire Place, Toronto, ON, M5S 3K7 (+1-416-946 0326) (pcj.programme@utoronto.ca) (www.munkschool.utoronto.ca/trudeaucentre).

United Nations Association in Canada / Association canadienne pour les Nations-Unies [UNAC/ACNU] (UN EL RE HR CD), 309 Cooper St - Suit 300, Ottawa, ON, K2P 0G5 (+1-613-232 5751) (fax 563 2455) (info@unac.org) (unac.org).

USCC Doukhobors (RP CD PA), Box 760, Grand Forks, BC, V0H 1H0 (+1-250-442 8252) (fax 442 3433) (info@uscctoukhobors.org) (www.uscctoukhobors.org). *Iskra*. Union of Spiritual Communities of Christ.

Voice of Women for Peace / La Voix des Femmes pour la Paix [VOW] (IB UN PA), 7 Labatt Ave - Suite 2121, Toronto, ON, M5A 1Z1 (+1-416-603 7915) (info@vowpeace.org) (www.vowpeace.org).

Women's International League for Peace and Freedom [WILPF] (WL), PO Box 365, 916 West Broadway, Vancouver, BC, V5Z 1K7 (+1-604-224 1517) (judydavis@telus.net).

World Federalist Movement - Canada / Mouvement Fédéraliste Mondial (Canada) (WF), Suite 207, 110 - 323 Chapel St, Ottawa, ON, K1N 7Z2 (+1-613-232 0647) (wfcnat@web.ca) (www.worldfederalistscanada.org). *Mondial*.

CHILE

Comité Nacional pro Defensa de la Flora y Fauna [CODEFF] (FE), Ernesto Reyes 035, Providencia, Santiago (+56-2-777 2534) (administra@codeff.cl) (www.codeff.cl).

Greenpeace Chile Pacífico Sur (GP), Argomedo 50, Santiago (+56-2-2634 2120) (fax 2634 8580) (info-chile@greenpeace.org) (www.greenpeace.org/chile).

Grupo de Objeción de Conciencia "Ni Casco Ni Uniforme" (WR), Bremen 585, Ñuñoa, Santiago (+56-2-556 6066) (objetores@yahoo.com) (nicasconiuniforme.wordpress.com).

Grupo de Objeción de Conciencia Rompiendo Filas (WR), Prat 289 - Oficina 2-A, Temuco (rompiendofilas@entodaspartes.org).

CHINA

Chinese Society of Radiation Medicine and Protection (IP), c/o Liu Zhi, Department of International Relations, Chinese Medical Association, 42 Dongsi Xidajie, Beijing 100710 (+86-10-8515 8136) (fax 8515 8551) (zhiliu@cma.org.cn) (www.cma.org.cn).

For explanation of codes and abbreviations, see introduction

Greenpeace China (GP), 3/F - Julong Office Building - Block 7, Julong Gardens, 68 Xinzhong St, Dongcheng District, Beijing 100027 (+86-10-6554 6931) (fax 6554 6932) (greenpeace.cn@greenpeace.org) (www.greenpeace.org/china). See also under Hong Kong for head office.

Natural Resources Defense Council [NRDC] (EL), Taikang Financial Tower - Suite 1706, Block 1 - 38 East 3rd Ring Rd, Chaoyang District, Beijing 100026 (+86-10-5927 0688) (www.nrdc.org). Office of US organisation NRDC (nrdcinfo@nrdc.org).

COLOMBIA

Acción Colectiva de Objetores y Objetoras de Conciencia [ACOOC] (WR), Cr 19 - No 33A - 26/1, Bogotá (+57-1-560 5058) (objecion@objetoresbogota.org) (objetoresbogota.org).

La Ruta Pacífica de las Mujeres, Carrera 35 - No 53A - 86, Bogotá (+57-1-222 9145) (www.rutapacifica.org.co).

Liga Internacional de Mujeres pro Paz y Libertad [LIMPAL] (WL), Calle 44 - No 19-28 - Of 201, Bogotá (+57-1-285 0062) (limpal@limpalcolombia.org) (limpalcolombia.org).

CONGO, DEMOCRATIC REPUBLIC OF

Cercle des Jeunes Leaders pour la Paix / Circle of Young Leaders for Peace (RP), Av Kwango - No 7, Kintambo Magasin, Ngaliema, Dist Lukunga, Kinshasa (+243-81-514 0938) (jcsaki2000@yahoo.fr).

Groupe Interconfessionnel de la Réconciliation / Kinshasa [GIR] (FR), see under Belgium.

Life & Peace Institute (CR RP), Bukavu (for postal address see under Rwanda) (pieter.vanholder@life-peace.org).

Ligue Internationale des Femmes pour la Paix et la Liberté [LIFPL] (WL), 11 Ave Ngandajika, Commune de Mont Ngafula, Kinshasa (+243-9900 32525) (wilpfdrcsection@gmail.com).

Peace & Conflict Resolution Project (CR), for postal address see under Rwanda (+243-993-463279) (peacecrp@yahoo.com) (www.peaceconflictresolutionproject.webs.com). Based in Bukavu.

COSTA RICA

Centro de Estudios Para la Paz [CEPPA] (RE), Apdo 8-4820, 1000 San José (+506-2234 0524) (fax) (info@ceppacr.org) (www.ceppacr.org).

Liga Internacional de Mujeres pro Paz y Libertad [LIMPAL] (WL), Avenida sexta Bis No 1336 - por Calle 15, Costado Oeste de los Tribunales San José (+506-2256 2406) (limpalcr@yahoo.es).

Monteverde Friends Meeting (SF), Monteverde 5655, Puntarenas (+506-2645 5530) (fax 2645 5302)

(MonteverdeQuakers@gmail.com)
(MonteverdeQuakers.org).
Religions for Peace - Costa Rica (RP), Apdo Postal 7288, 1000 San Jose (eduardoenrique_69@msn.com).

CROATIA

Antiratna kampanja Hrvatske / Anti-War Campaign Croatia [ARK] (PA HR), Nazarova 1, 10000 Zagreb (+385-1-484 8720) (fax) (ark@zamir.net). CO counselling and anti-war work.

Centar za žene žrtve Rata / Centre for Women War Victims [ROSA] (CR HR), Kralja Držislava 2, 10000 Zagreb (+385-1-455 1142) (fax 455 1128) (cenzena@zamir.net) (www.czzzr.hr). Feminist, anti-militarist.

Centar Za Mir, Nenasilje i Ljudska Prava - Osijek / Centre for Peace, Nonviolence and Human Rights (CR HR PC RE), Trg Augusta Šenoe 1, 31000 Osijek (+385-31-206886) (fax 206889) (centar-za-mir@centar-za-mir.hr) (www.centar-za-mir.hr).

Centar za Mirovne Studije / Centre for Peace Studies [CMS] (WR CR RE HR), Selska cesta 112a, 10000 Zagreb (+385-1-482 0094) (fax) (cms@cms.hr) (www.cms.hr).

Dalmatinski Komitet za Ljudska Prava [DK] (HR), Trumbučac 19, 21000 Split (+385-21-482805) (dkomit@cryptolab.net) (dalmatinskikomitet.com). Dalmatian Committee for Human Rights.

CUBA

Movimiento Cubano por la Paz y la Soberanía de los Pueblos (WP), Calle 18 No 704, e/ 7ma y 9na, Miramar Playa, La Habana (+53-7-832 0490) (fax 833 3860) (movpaz@enet.cu) (www.movpaz.org).

CYPRUS

Conciliation - Peace Economics Network (CR), PO Box 20209, Nicosia 1665 (costas@highwaycommunications.com).

Hands Across the Divide - Women Building Bridges in Cyprus (HR CD CR DA), Ellispontos 15, Dasoupolis 2015, Nicosia (handsacrossthedivide@gmail.com) (www.handsacrossthedivide.org). Supports feminist values and demilitaristion.

Oikologiki Kinisi Kyprou / Ecological Movement of Cyprus (EL), TK 28948, Nicosia 2084 (+357-2251 8787) (fax 2251 2710) (ecological_movement@cytanet.com.cy) (www.ecologicalmovement.org.cy). *Ecologiki Enimerosi.*

CYPRUS (NORTHERN)

Hands Across the Divide - Women Building Bridges in Cyprus (HR CD CR DA), see under Cyprus (www.handsacrossthedivide.org). Supports feminist values and demilitaristion.

CZECH REPUBLIC

Amnesty International Česká Republika [AI ČR] (AI), Provaznická 3, 11000 Praha 1 (+420-2 2424 3600) (amnesty@amnesty.cz) (www.amnesty.cz).

České Mírové Hnutí / Czech Peace Movement (WP), Josefa Houdka 123, 15531 Praha (mirovehnuti@email.cz) (www.mirovehnuti.cz).

Hnutí DUHA (FE RA), Údolní 33, 60200 Brno (+420-5 4521 4431) (fax 5 4521 4429) (info@hnutiduha.cz) (hnutiduha.cz). *Evergreen.*

Nezávislé Sociálně Ekologické Hnutí / Independent Social-Ecological Movement [NESEHNUTÍ] (EL HR AT), třída Kpt Jaroše 18, 60200 Brno (+420-5 4324 5342) (brno@nesehnuti.cz) (www.nesehnuti.cz).

Physicians for Global Security - Czech Section of IPPNW (IP), c/o Vaclav Stukavec, Jírhí 222, 46801 Jablonec nad Nisou 8 (stukavr@volny.cz).

DENMARK

Aldrig Mere Krig [AMK] (WR AT IB), Nørremarksvej 4, 6880 Tarm (+45-9737 3163) (amk@fred.dk) (www.fred.dk/amk/). *Ikkevold.*

Amnesty International (AI), Gammeltorv 8 - 5 sal, 1457 København K (+45-3345 6565) (amnesty@amnesty.dk) (www.amnesty.dk).

Center for Konfliktløsning / Danish Centre for Conflict Resolution (CR RE), Dronning Olgas Vej 30, 2000 Frederiksberg (+45-3520 0550) (center@konfliktloesning.dk) (www.konfliktloesning.dk).

Danske Laeger Mod Kernevåben [DLMK] (IP), Langdalsvej 40, 8220 Brabrand, Aarhus (+45-8626 4717) (povl.revsbech@gmail.com) (www.dlmk.dk). *Danske Laeger Mod Kernevåben.*

FN-Forbundet (UN WF), Tordenskjoldsgade 25 st th, 1055 København K (+45-3346 4690) (fax 3646 4649) (fnforbundet@fnforbundet.dk) (www.fnforbundet.dk).

Green Cross Denmark (EL TW DA HR), Abel Cathrines Gade 3 - 1 sal, 1654 København V (+45-2639 1555) (kbi@greencross.dk) (greencross.dk).

Kvaekercentret (SF), Drejervej 15 - 4, 2400 København NV.

Kvindernes Internationale Liga for Fred og Frihed [KILFF] (WL RE), Vesterbrogade 10 - 2, 1620 København V (+45-3323 1097) (wilpfdk@gmail.com) (kvindefredsliga.dk).

Servas Danmark (SE), c/o Jan Degrauwe, Højbakkevej 32, 9440 Aabybro (+45-2048 5087) (info@servas.dk) (www.servas.dk).

Worldwatch Institute Europe (EL AT), Strandgade 12B, 1401 København K (+45-2087 1933) (info@worldwatch-europe.org) (www.worldwatch-europe.org). Main office in USA (+1-202-745 8092).

EAST TIMOR

EAST TIMOR

Haburas Foundation / Friends of the Earth Timor Leste (FE), PO Box 390, Dili (+670-331 0103) (haburaslorosae@yahoo.com) (www.haburasfoundation.org).

La'o Hamutuk - Instituto ba Analiza no Monitor Dezenvolvimento iha Timor-Leste (TW EL), PO Box 340, Dili (+670-332 1040) (info@laohamutuk.org) (www.laohamutuk.org).

EGYPT

Arab Organisation for Human Rights [AOHR] (HR), 91 Merghani St, Heliopolis, Cairo 11341 (+20-2-2418 1396) (fax 2418 5346) (alaa.shalaby@aohr.net) (www.aohr.net).

EL SALVADOR

Centro Salvadoreño de Tecnología Apropiada [CESTA] (FE), Apdo 3065, San Salvador (+503-2213 1400) (fax 2220 6479) (cesta@cesta-foe.org.sv) (www.cesta-foe.org.sv).

ESTONIA

Eestimaa Roheliseid / Estonian Green Party (EL), Postkast 4740, 13503 Tallinn (+372-502 6816) (info@erakond.ee) (www.erakond.ee).

Noortevahetuse Arengu ühing / Youth Exchange Development Association [EstYES] (SC), Wedemanni 3, Tallinn 10126 (+372-601 3098) (fax 601 3309) (estyes@estyes.ee) (www.estyes.ee).

United Nations Association of Estonia (UN), Veski 42, 50409 Tartu (+372-527 1051) (una.estonia@gmail.com) (www.una.ee).

ETHIOPIA

Life & Peace Institute - Ethiopia Regional Programme (CR RP), Wollo Sefer, Ethio-China Friendship Avenue, Addis Ababa (+251-11-551 3670) (fax 551 1291) (hannah.tsadik@life-peace.org).

FIJI

Greenpeace Pacific - Fiji Office (GP), 1st Floor, Old Town Hall, Victoria Parade, Suva (+679-331 2861) (fax 331 2784) (support.au@greenpeace.org).

FINLAND

Ålands Fredsinstitut / Åland Islands Peace Institute (RE HR CR), PB 85, 22101 Mariehamn, Åland (+358-18-15570) (peace@peace.ax) (www.peace.ax).

Civil Society Conflict Prevention Network [KATU] (CR DA), TÖÖlÖntorinkatu 2B - 4 krs, 00260 Helsinki (+358-9-2315 0550) (fax 2315 0520) (info@katunet.fi) (www.katunet.fi).

Greenpeace Finland (GP), Iso Roobertinkatu 20-22 A (5 frs), 00120 Helsinki (+358-9-6229 2200) (fax 6229 2222) (info.finland@greenpeace.org) (www.greenpeace.fi).

Maan Ystävät / Friends of the Earth (FE), Mechelininkatu 36b, 00260 Helsinki (toimisto@maanystavat.fi) (www.maanystavat.fi).

Peace Union of Finland / Suomen Rauhanliitto / Finlands FredsfÖrbundet (IB FR ND AT RE), Peace Station, Veturitori, 00520 Helsinki (+358-9-7568 2828) (fax 147297) (rauhanliitto@rauhanliitto.fi).

Suomen Luonnonsuojeluliitto / Finnish Association for Nature Conservation [FANC] (EL), Itälahdenkatu 22-b A, 00210 Helsinki (+358-9-2280 8224) (toimisto@sll.fi) (www.sll.fi).

Tampere Peace Research Institute [TAPRI] (RE), University of Tampere, 33014 (+358-3-3551 7696) (fax 223 6620) (unto.vesa@uta.fi) (www.uta.fi/tapri).

Union of Conscientious Objectors / Aseistakieltäytyjäliitto [AKL] (WR), Rauhanasema, Veturitori 3, 00520 Helsinki (+358-9-7568 2444) (fax 147297) (toimisto@akl-web.fi) (www.akl-web.fi).

Women's International League for Peace and Freedom - Finnish Section [WILPF] (WL), PL 1174, 00101 Helsinki (wilpf@wilpf.fi) (wilpf.fi).

FRANCE

Action des Chrétiens pour l'Abolition de la Torture [ACAT] (HR), 7 rue Georges Lardennois, 75019 Paris (+33-14040 4243) (fax 14040 4244) (acat@acatfrance.fr) (www.acatfrance.fr).

Action des Citoyens pour le Désarmement Nucléaire [ACDN] (ND), 31 Rue du Cormier, 17100 Saintes (+33-673 507661) (contact@acdn.net) (www.acdn.net). Opposes both military and civilian nukes.

Alternatives Non-Violentes [ANV] (PA RE CR), Centre 308, 82 rue Jeanne d'Arc, 76000 Rouen (+33-235 752344) (contact@alternatives-non-violentes.org) (alternatives-non-violentes.org).

Amis de la Terre - France (FE), Mundo M, 47 ave Pasteur, 93100 Montreuil (+33-14851 3222) (secretariat@amisdelaterre.org) (www.amisdelaterre.org).

Association des Médecins Français pour la Prévention de la Guerre Nucléaire [AMFPGN] (IP), 5 Rue Las Cases, 75007 Paris (+33-14336 7781) (fax) (revue@amfpgn.org) (www.amfpgn.org). *Médecine et Guerre Nucléaire.*

Association française pour les Nations Unies (UN), 26 Av Charles Floquet, 75007 Paris (+33-17716 2454) (contact@afnu.fr) (afnu.fr).

Brigades de Paix Internationales [PBI-France] (HR PO RE CD), 21 ter rue Voltaire, 75011 Paris (+33-14373 4960) (pbi.france@free.fr) (www.pbi-france.org).

Centre Français d'Enregistrement des Citoyens du Monde (WF), 15 rue Victor Duruy, 75015 Paris (+33-14531 2999) (contact@citoyensdumonde.net) (www.citoyensdumonde.net). *Citoyens du Monde.*

Cesser d'Alimenter la Guerre / Stop Fuelling War [SFW] (AT RA), c/o Centre Quaker de Paris, 114 rue de Vaugirard, 75006 Paris (stopfuellingwar@gmail.com) (stopfuellingwar.org).
Countering the normalisation of the trade in arms.

Collectif des Objectrices et Objecteurs Tarnais [COT] (WR), c/o Sophie Flaquet, Arvieu, 81190 Tanus (cot@cot81.com) (cot81.com).

Commission de Recherche et d'Information Indépendantes sur la Radioactivité [CRIIRAD] (EL PO), Le Cime, 471 Av Victor Hugo, 26000 Valence (+33-475 418250) (fax 475 812648) (contact@criirad.org) (www.criirad.org).
Le Trait d'Union.

Coordination de l'Action Non-Violente de l'Arche [CANVA] (RP), La Presle, 18360 Vesdun (webcanva@laposte.net) (www.canva.fr).

Coordination pour l'éducation à la Non-violence et la Paix (RE), 148 du Faubourg Saint-Denis, 75010 Paris (+33-14633 4156) (education-nvp.org).

église et Paix (RP), c/o Louise & Bernadette Joly, 5 rue du Mont Verdun, 69140 Rillieux la Pape (+33-478 888725) (fax) (EglisePaix@church-and-peace.org).

Europe écologie - Les Verts (EL), 6 rue Chaudron, 75010 Paris (+33-15319 5319) (eelv.fr). Successor party to Les Verts.

Fédération Mères Pour la Paix (HR TW), BP 728, 59655 Villeneuve d'Ascq cedex (www.merespourlapaix.org).

Gandhi International (RE), c/o Louis Campana, 37 rue de la Concorde, 11000 Carcassonne (gandhiji2012@gmail.com) (www.gandhi2012.org).

Greenpeace (GP), 13 rue d'Enghien, 75010 Paris (+33-18096 9696) (fax) (contact.fr@greenpeace.org) (www.greenpeace.org/france).

Groupement pour les Droits des Minorités [GDM] (HR), 212 rue St-Martin, 75003 Paris (+33-14575 0137) (fax 14579 8046) (yplasseraud@wanadoo.fr).
La Lettre du GDM.

Institut de Recherche sur la Résolution Non-violente des Conflits [IRNC] (RE SD CR PA), 14 rue des Meuniers, 93100 Montreuil-sous-Bois (+33-14287 9469) (fax) (irnc@irnc.org) (www.irnc.org).
Alternatives Non-violentes.

Ligue Internationale des Femmes pour la Paix et la Liberté - Section française [LIFPL/WILPF] (WL ND RE), 114 rue de Vaugirard, 75006 Paris (+33-14844 6711) (wilpf-france.net).

Mémorial de Caen Museum - Cité de l'Histoire pour la Paix / Centre for History and Peace (PO RE), Esplanade Eisenhower, BP 55026, 14050 Caen Cedex 4 (+33-231 060644) (fax 231 060670) (contact@memorial-caen.fr) (www.memorial-caen.fr).

Mouvement de la Paix (IB WP ND PA AT), 9 Rue Dulcie September, 93400 Saint-Ouen (+33-14012 0912) (national@mvtpaix.org) (www.mvtpaix.org).
Planète Paix; La Paix en Mouvement.

Mouvement International de la Réconciliation [MIR] (FR WR), 68 rue de Babylone, 75007 Paris (+33-14753 8405) (mirfr@club-internet.fr) (www.mirfrance.org).
Cahiers de la Réconciliation.

Mouvement pour une Alternative Non-violente [MAN] (WR SD CR AT RA), 47 ave Pasteur, 93100 Montreuil (+33-14544 4825) (man@nonviolence.fr) (www.nonviolence.fr).
Non-Violence Actualité [NVA], Centre de Ressources sur la Gestion non-violente des Relations et des Conflits, BP 241, 45202 Montargis cedex (+33-238 936722) (fax 975 385985) (Nonviolence.Actualite@wanadoo.fr) (www.nonviolence-actualite.org). 6 yrly, €43 pa.

Pax Christi France (PC), 5 rue Morère, 75014 Paris (+33-14449 0636) (accueil@paxchristi.cef.fr) (www.paxchristi.cef.fr). *Journal de la Paix.*

Peace Lines / Messageries de la Paix (CR RE), 51310 Esternay (+33-326 819115) (peacelines@gmail.com) (www.peacelines.org).
The Messengers' Mail / Le Courrier des Messageries.

Réseau "Sortir du Nucléaire" / Network for a Nuclear Phase-Out (EL RA PO), 9 rue Dumenge, 69317 Lyon cedex 04 (+33-47828 2922) (fax 47207 7004) (contact@sortirdunucleaire.org) (www.sortirdunucleaire.org). Network of groups in France against nuclear energy.

Religions pour la Paix (RP), 8 bis Rue Jean Bart, 75006 Paris (Religionspourlapaix@yahoo.fr) (religionspourlapaix.org).

Service Civil International [SCI-F] (SC), 75 rue du Chevalier Français, 59800 Lille (+33-320 552258) (sci@sci-france.org) (www.sci-france.org).

Silence (EL AL PA PO), 9 Rue Dumenge, 69317 Lyon cedex 04 (+33-478 395533) (www.revuesilence.net). Mthly, €55 pa.

Société Religieuse des Amis (SF), Centre Quaker International, 114 Rue de Vaugirard, 75006 Paris (+33-14548 7423) (assembleedefrance@gmail.com) (www.QuakersEnFrance.org).
Lettre des Amis.

Solidarités Jeunesses (WC CD), 10 Rue du 8 Mai 1945, 75010 Paris (+33-15526 8877) (fax 15326 0326) (secretariat@solidaritesjeunesses.org) (www.solidaritesjeunesses.org).

Sortir de la Violence - France (RP), 11 rue de la Chaise, 75007 Paris (sdv-France@sortirdelaviolence.org) (www.sortirdelaviolence.org).

FRANCE

Union Pacifiste de France [UPF] (WR AT), BP 40196, 75624 Paris cédex 13 (+33-14586 0875) (union.pacifiste@orange.fr) (www.unionpacifiste.org). *Union Pacifiste.*

FRENCH POLYNESIA

Ligue Internationale des Femmes pour la Paix et la Liberté - Section Polynésienne [LIFPL] (WL), Faaone pk 49.2, Côté Montagne, 98713 Faaone, Tahiti (+689-264729) (wilpf.polynesie@gmail.com).

GERMANY

13 Februar 1945 (CR DA), Postfach 160232, 01288 Dresden (info@dresden-1945.de) (www.dresden-1945.de).

Aktion der Christen für die Abschaffung der Folter [ACAT] (HR), Postfach 1114, 59331 Lüdinghausen (+49-2591-7533) (fax 70527) (ACAT.eV@t-online.de) (www.acat-deutschland.de).

Aktion Sühnezeichen Friedensdienste [ASF] (WC RP HR CD), Auguststr 80, 10117 Berlin-Mitte (+49-30-2839 5184) (fax 2839 5135) (asf@asf-ev.de) (www.asf-ev.de). *Zeichen.*

Aktionsgemeinschaft Dienst für den Frieden [AGDF] (WC PA RP), Endenicher Str 41, 53115 Bonn (+49-228-249990) (fax 249 9920) (agdf@friedensdienst.de) (www.friedensdienst.de). *Voluntary service co-ordination agency.*

Amnesty International (AI), Zinnowitzer Str 1, 10115 Berlin (+49-30-420 2480) (fax 4202 48488) (info@amnesty.de) (www.amnesty.de). *ai-Journal.*

Anti-Kriegs-Museum / Anti-War Museum (WR), Brüsseler Str 21, 13353 Berlin (+49-30-4549 0110) (Anti-Kriegs-Museum@gmx.de) (www.anti-kriegs-museum.de).

Arbeitsgemeinschaft für Friedens- und Konfliktforschung / German Association for Peace and Conflict Studies [AFK] (RE), c/o Lehrstül für Friedens- und Konfliktforschung, Universität Augsburg, 86135 Augsburg (+49-821-598 5553) (fax 598 5720) (afk-gf@afk-web.de) (www.afk-web.de).

Archiv Aktiv für gewaltfreie Bewegungen (WR RE EL), Normannenweg 17-21, 20537 Hamburg (+49-40-430 2046) (email@archiv-aktiv.de) (www.archiv-aktiv.de).

ausgestrahlt (EL RA ND), Grosse Bergstr 189, 22767 Hamburg (+49-40-2531 3913) (fax 2531 8944) (info@ausgestrahlt.de) (www.ausgestrahlt.de). *.ausgestrahlt-magazin.* Anti-nuclear direct action network.

Bürgermeister für den Frieden in Deutschland und Österreich (CD ND DA), c/o Landeshauptstadt Hannover, Büro Oberbürgermeister, Trammplatz 2, 30159 Hannover (+49-511-1684 1446) (fax 1684 4025) (mayorsforpeace@hannover-stadt.de) (www.mayorsforpeace.de).

Berghof Foundation (CR RE), Altensteinstr 48a, 14195 Berlin (+49-30-844 1540) (fax 8441 5499) (info@berghof-conflictresearch.org) (www.berghof-conflictresearch.org). Works to prevent political and social violence.

Bund für Soziale Verteidigung [BSV] (WR SD CR), Schwarzer Weg 8, 32423 Minden (+49-571-29456) (fax 23019) (info@soziale-verteidigung.de) (www.soziale-verteidigung.de). *Soziale Verteidigung.*

Bund für Umwelt und Naturschutz Deutschland [BUND] (FE), Am Köllnischen Park 1, 10179 Berlin (+49-30-275 8640) (fax 2758 6440) (bund@bund.net) (www.bund.net). *BUNDmagazin.*

Connection eV (PA HR), Von-Behring-Str 110, 63075 Offenbach (+49-69-8237 5534) (fax 8237 5535) (office@Connection-eV.org) (www.Connection-eV.org). *KDV im Krieg.* International work for COs and deserters.

Deutsch-Russischer Austausch / Nyemyetsko-Russkiy Obmyen [DRA] (CD), Badstr 44, 13357 Berlin (+49-30-446 6800) (fax 4466 8010) (info@austausch.org) (www.austausch.org). German-Russian Exchange.

Deutsche Friedens-Bücherei (RE PA EL), Postfach 101361, 66013 Saarbrücken (+33-387 950018).

Deutsche Friedensgesellschaft - Internationale der Kriegsdienstgegner [DFG-IdK] (WR DA), Jungfrauenthal 37, 20149 Hamburg (+49-40-453433) (fax 4440 5270) (info@dfg-idk.de) (www.dfg-idk.de). *Rundbrief.*

Deutsche Friedensgesellschaft - Vereinigte Kriegsdienstgegner [DFG-VK] (WR IB RE), Werastr 10, 70182 Stuttgart (+49-711-5189 2626) (fax 2486 9622) (office@dfg-vk.de) (www.dfg-vk.de).

Deutsche Gesellschaft für die Vereinten Nationen [DGVN] (UN), Zimmerstr 26/27, 10969 Berlin (+49-30-259 3750) (fax 2593 7529) (info@dgvn.de) (www.dgvn.de). *Vereinte Nationen.*

Deutsche Sektion der IPPNW / ärzte in sozialer Verantwortung (IPPNW Germany) (IP AT DA), Körtestr 10, 10967 Berlin (+49-30-698 0740) (fax 693 8166) (ippnw@ippnw.de) (www.ippnw.de). *Forum.*

Deutscher Friedensrat / German Peace Council (WP), Platz der Vereinten Nationen 7, 10249 Berlin (+49-30-426 5290) (fax 4201 7338) (saefkow-berlin@t-online.de) (www.deutscher-friedensrat.de).

Deutsches Bündnis Kindersoldaten (HR PA), c/o Kindernothilfe, Düsseldorfer Landstr 180, 47249 Duisburg (+49-203-778 9111) (fax 778 9118) (info@kindernothilfe.de) (www.kindernothilfe.de). Campaigns against use of child soldiers.

Evangelische Arbeitsgemeinschaft für Kriegsdienstverweigerung und Frieden [EAK] (RP), Endenicher Str 41, 53115 Bonn (+49-228-249990) (fax 249 9920) (office@eak-online.de) (www.eak-online.de). Protestant Association for the Care of COs.

Forum Ziviler Friedensdienst / Civil Peace Service Forum [forumZFD] (SF IP CR RE), Am Kölner Brett 8, 50825 Köln (+49-221-912 7320) (fax 9127 3299) (kontakt@forumZFD.de) (www.forumZFD.de). Offers conflict transformation training & courses.

Frauennetzwerk für Frieden (IB), Kaiserstr 8, 53113 Bonn (+49-228-626730) (fax 626780) (fn.frieden@t-online.de) (www.frauennetzwerk-fuer-frieden.de).

Friedens- und Begegnungsstätte Mutlangen (ND WC CR), Forststr 3, 73557 Mutlangen (+49-7171-75661) (fax) (post@pressehuette.de) (www.pressehuette.de). FreiRaum.

Friedensausschuss der Religiösen Gesellschaft der Freunde (Quäker) (SF PA CR DA), Föhrenstieg 8, 22926 Ahrensburg (+49-4102-53337) (helga.tempel@gmx.de). Quäker.

Galtung Institute for Peace Theory and Peace Practice (GI) (RE CR TW), Markgraffenstr 42a, 79639 Grenzach-Wyhlen (+49-7624-912 9137) (info@galtung-institute.com) (www.galtung-institute.com). Previously Gandhi-Informations-Zentrum.

Gandhi Information Centre (PA RE), Postfach 210109, 10501 Berlin (mkgandhi@snafu.de) (www.nonviolent-resistance.info). Previously Gandhi-Informations-Zentrum.

GandhiServe Foundation (RE HR), Rathausstr 51a, 12105 Berlin (+49-30-705 4054) (fax 3212-100 3676) (mail@gandhimail.org) (www.gandhiserve.com).

Gewaltfreie Aktion Atomwaffen Abschaffen / Nonviolent Action to Abolish Nuclear Weapons [GAAA] (ND RA), c/o Marion Küpker, Beckstr 14, 20357 Hamburg (+49-40-430 7332) (marion.kuepker@gaaa.org) (www.gaaa.org).

Graswurzelrevolution (WR AL RA), Breul 43, 48143 Münster (+49-251-482 9057) (fax 482 9032) (redaktion@graswurzel.net) (www.graswurzel.net).

Greenpeace (GP), Hongkongstr 10, 20457 Hamburg (+49-40-306180) (fax 3061 8100) (mail@greenpeace.de) (www.greenpeace.de). Berlin: +49-30-308 8990.

Hessische Stiftung Friedens- und Konfliktforschung / Peace Research Institute Frankfurt [HSFK/PRIF] (RE), Baseler Str 27-31, 60329 Frankfurt (+49-69-959 1040) (fax 558481) (info@hsfk.de) (www.hsfk.de). HSFK-Standpunkt.

Humanistische Union [HU] (HR), Haus der Demokratie und Menschenrechte, Greifswalder Str 4, 10405 Berlin (+49-30-2045 0256) (fax 2045 0257) (info@humanistische-union.de) (www.humanistische-union.de). Vorgänge.

Informationsstelle Militarisierung [IMI] (PA RE AT), Hechingerstr 203, 72072 Tübingen (+49-7071-49154) (fax 49159) (imi@imi-online.de) (www.imi-online.de). Ausdruck.

Iniciativa Angolana Antimilitarista para os Direitos Humanos [IAADH] (WR HR), Flughafenstr 21, 12053 Berlin (+49-30-3462 0468) (fax 3462 0469) (info@iaadh.de) (www.iaadh.de). Angolan Antimilitarist Initiative for Human Rights.

Initiative Kirche von unten [IKvu] (RP TW HR), c/o Evangelische Hoffnungsgemeinde, Hafenstr 5, 60327 Frankfurt am Main (www.ikvu.de).

Initiative Musiker/innen gegen Auftritte der Bundeswehrmusikkorps (PA), c/o Dietmar Parchow, Austr 77, 72669 Unterensingen (musikergegenmilitaermusik@idk-berlin.de) (musiker-gegen-militaermusik.jimdo.com). Against public and church use of military bands.

Institut für Friedensarbeit und Gewaltfreie Konfliktaustragung [IFGK] (WR RE CR), Hauptstr 35, 55491 Wahlenau/Hunsrück (+49-6543-980096) (fax 500636) (BMuellerIFGK@t-online.de) (www.ifgk.de). IFGK Working Papers.

Institut für Friedenspädagogik Tübingen/ Institute for Peace Education Tübingen (RE CR), Corrensstr 12, 72076 Tübingen (+49-7071-920510) (fax 920 5111) (info-tuebingen@berghof-foundation.org) (www.friedenspaedagogik.de). A branch of the Berghof Foundation.

Institute for International Assistance and Solidarity [IFIAS] (IB CD HR ND), Postfach 170420, 53027 Bonn (+49-228-721 6864) (fax 721 6866) (drake@ifias.eu) (www.ifias.eu). Also in Belgium.

Internationale der KriegsdienstgegnerInnen [IDK] (WR AL), Postfach 280312, 13443 Berlin (info@idk-berlin.de) (www.idk-info.net).

Internationale Frauenliga für Frieden und Freiheit [IFFF] (WL), Haus der Demokratie und Menschenrechte, Greifswalder Str 4, 10405 Berlin (info@wilpf.de) (www.wilpf.de).

Internationale Jugendgemeinschaftsdienste [IJGD] (WC EL CD), Kasernenstr 48, 53111 Bonn (+49-228-228 0014) (fax 228 0010) (workcamps@ijgd.de) (www.ijgd.de). Workcamps and volunteering in Germany and abroad.

Juristen und Juristinnen gegan Atomare, Biologische und Chemische Waffen - IALANA Deutschland (ND), Marienstr 19-20, 10117 Berlin (+49-30-2065 4857) (fax 2065 4858) (info@ialana.de) (www.ialana.de).

GERMANY

Kampagne gegen Wehrpflicht, Zwangsdienste und Militär (PA RA SD), Kopenhagener Str 71, 10437 Berlin (+49-30-4401 3025) (fax 4401 3029) (info@kampagne.de) (www.kampagne.de).

Komitee für Grundrechte und Demokratie (HR CD RA PA), Aquinostr 7-11 (HH), 50670 Köln (+49-221-972 6920) (fax 972 6931) (info@grundrechtekomitee.de) (www.grundrechtekomitee.de).

Kooperation für den Frieden (DA ND RE), Römerstr 88, 53111 Bonn (+49-228-692905) (fax 692906) (info@koop-frieden.de) (www.koop-frieden.de). Networking organisation in German peace movement.

KURVE Wustrow - Bildungs- und Begegnungsstätte für gewaltfreie Aktion (FR PA CR HR RE), Kirchstr 14, 29462 Wustrow (+49-5843-98710) (fax 987111) (info@kurvewustrow.org) (www.kurvewustrow.org).

Martin-Luther-King-Zentrum, Stadtgutstr 23, 08412 Werdau (+49-3761-760284) (fax 760304) (info@martin-luther-king-zentrum.de) (www.king-zentrum.de).

Netzwerk Friedenskooperative (ND PA AT), Römerstr 88, 53111 Bonn (+49-228-692904) (fax 692906) (friekoop@friedenskooperative.de) (www.friedenskooperative.de). Friedensforum.

Netzwerk Friedenssteuer [NWFS] (TR), Krennerweg 12, 81479 München (+49-8062-725 2395) (fax 725 2396) (info@netzwerk-friedenssteuer.de) (www.netzwerk-friedenssteuer.de). Friedenssteuer-Nachrichten.

Ohne Rüstung Leben (AT CR PA ND DA), Arndtstr 31, 70197 Stuttgart (+49-711-608396) (fax 608357) (orl@gaia.de) (www.ohne-ruestung-leben.de). Ohne Rüstung Leben-Informationen.

Pax Christi Deutsche Sektion (PC), Hedwigskirchgasse 3, 10117 Berlin (+49-30-2007 6780) (fax 2007 67819) (sekretariat@paxchristi.de) (www.paxchristi.de).

Peace Brigades International Deutscher Zweig [PBI] (CR HR PA), Bahrenfelderstr 101 A, 22765 Hamburg (+49-40-3890 4370) (fax 3890 43729) (info@pbi-deutschland.de) (www.pbideutschland.de).

Pestizid Aktions-Netzwerk [PAN Germany] (EL), Nernstweg 32, 22765 Hamburg (+49-40-3991 9100) (fax 3991 91030) (info@pan-germany.org) (www.pan-germany.org).

RüstungsInformationsBüro [RIB-Büro] (AT PA RE), Stühlinger Str 7, 79016 Freiburg (+49-761-767 8088) (fax 767 8089) (rib@rib-ev.de) (www.rib-ev.de). Campaign against small arms.

RfP Deutschland / Religions for Peace (RP), c/o Franz Brendle, Im Schellenkönig 61, 70184 Stuttgart (+49-711-539 0209) (fax 505 8648) (rfp@r-f-p.de) (www.religionsforpeace.de). Informationen.

Stiftung die schwelle / Schwelle Foundation - Beiträge zum Frieden (CR TW RE HR), Wachmannstr 79, 28209 Bremen (+49-421-303 2575) (fax 303 2464) (stiftung@dieschwelle.de) (www.dieschwelle.de).

Terre des Femmes - Menschenrechte für die Frau eV (HR), Brunnenstr 128, 13355 Berlin (+49-30-4050 46990) (fax 4050 469999) (info@frauenrechte.de) (www.frauenrechte.de).

Versöhnungsbund [VB] (FR IB PA), Schwarzer Weg 8, 32423 Minden (+49-571-850875) (fax 829 2387) (vb@versoehnungsbund.de) (www.versoehnungsbund.de).

Working Group on Conscientious Objection to War (WR), c/o Franz Nadler, Riethgasse 4, 63075 Offenbach (+49-69-815128) (fax) (office@connection-eV.org) (www.connection-eV.de). KDV im Krieg.

Zentralstelle für Recht und Schutz der Kriegsdienstverweigerer aus Gewissensgründen (HR), Sielstr 40, 26345 Bockhorn (+49-4453-986 4888) (fax 986 4890) (Zentralstelle.KDV@t-online.de) (www.Zentralstelle-KDV.de).

GHANA

Amnesty International [AI Ghana] (AI), Private Mail Bag, Accra-North (+233-30-222 0814) (fax 222 0805) (info@amnestyghana.org) (amnestyghana.org).

Friends of the Earth - Ghana [FoE] (FE), Private Mail Bag, General Post Office, Accra (+233-30-254 4257) (fax) (info@foe-gh.org) (www.foe-gh.org).

United Nations Association of Ghana (UN), Private Mail Bag, Ministries Post Office, Accra (+233-30-376 8858) (office@unaghana.org) (www.unaghana.org).

West Africa Network for Peacebuilding - Ghana (RE), PO Box CT 4434, Cantonments, Accra (+233-30-277 5975) (fax 277 6018).

GREECE

Diethnis Amnistia / Amnesty International (AI), 30 Sina Street, 10672 Athinai (+30-210 3600 628) (fax 210 3638 016) (athens@amnesty.org.gr) (www.amnesty.org.gr). Martyries.

Elliniki Epitropi gia ti Thiethni Yphesi kai Eirene / Greek Committee for International Detente and Peace [EEDYE] (WP), Themistokleous 48, 10681 Athinai (+30-210 3844 853) (fax 210 3844 879) (eedye@otenet.gr) (eedye.gr).

Enomenes Koinonies ton Valkanion / United Scieties of the Balkans [USB] (CD CR HR), Adamanas 9, Agios Paulos, 55438 Thessaloniki (+30-231 0215 629) (fax) (info@usbngo.gr) (www.usbngo.gr).

Greenpeace Greece (GP), Kolonou 78, 10437
Athinai (+30-210 3840 774)
(fax 210 3804 008)
(gpgreece@greenpeace.org)
(www.greenpeace.org/greece).

Kinisi Ethelonton / Volunteer Movement [SCI-
Hellas] (SC), Pythagora 12, Neos Kosmos,
11743 Athinai (+30-215 5406 504)
(info@sci.gr) (www.sci.gr).

Oikologoi Prasinoi / Ecologist Greens (EL),
Plateia Eleftherias 14, 10553 Athinai
(+30-210 3306 301) (fax 210 3241 825)
(ecogreen@otenet.gr) (www.ecogreens.gr).
Green Party.

Syndhesmos Antirrision Syneidhisis /
Association of Greek Conscientious
Objectors [SAS] (WR), Tsamadou 13A,
10683 Athinai (+30-694 4542 228)
(fax 210 4622 753) (greekCO@hotmail.com)
(www.antirrisies.gr).

HAITI

Pax Christi (PC), 2 - Marassa 12, Croix-des-
Bouquets (+509-2511 4585) (fax 2246 3469)
(paxchristihaiti@yahoo.fr).

HONG KONG

Alternatives to Violence Project - AVP Hong
Kong (CR PO), 12a Shun Ho Tower, 24-30
Ice House St, Central
(avphongkong@gmail.com)
(www.avphongkong.org).

Amnesty International Hong Kong (AI), Unit
3D, Best-O-Best Commercial Centre, 32-36
Ferry St, Kowloon (+852-2300 1250)
(fax 2782 0583) (admin-hk@amnesty.org.hk)
(www.amnesty.org.hk).

Association for the Advancement of Feminism
[AAF] (HR), Flats 119-120, Lai Yeung House,
Lei Cheng Uk Estate, Kowloon (+852-2720
0891) (fax 2720 0205) (hkaaf38@gmail.com)
(www.aaf.org.hk). Nuliu.

Greenpeace China (GP), 8/F Pacific Plaza,
410-418 Des Voeux Rd West
(+852-2854 8300) (fax 2745 2426)
(enquiry.hk@greenpeace.org)
(www.greenpeace.org/china).
Also Beijing office: see under China.

Human Rights in China - Hong Kong Office
[HRIC] (HR), GPO, PO Box 1778
(+852-2701 8021) (hrichk@hrichina.org)
(www.hrichina.org).
Main office in New York (+1-212-239 4495).

HUNGARY

ACAT-Hungary (HR), c/o Csaba Kábódi,
Eötvos University, Egyetem Tér 1-3, 1364
Budapest (+36-1-252 5961) (fax)
(kabodi@ajk.elte.hu).

Bocs Foundation (FR EL TW), Pf 7, 8003
Székesfehérvár (m@bocs.hu)
(www.bocs.hu). Bocsmagazin.

Egyház és Béke (RP RE HR), Pf 7, 8003
Székesfehérvár
(Reg.East@church-and-peace.org).

ICELAND

Amnesty International (AI), Thingholtsstraeti
27, 101 Reykjavík (+354-511 7900) (fax 511
7901) (amnesty@amnesty.is)
(www.amnesty.is).

Peace 2000 Institute (CR RE), Vogasel 1, 109
Reykjavík (+354-557 1000) (fax 496 2005)
(info@peace2000.org) (peace2000.org).
Offices also in Britain, USA.

INDIA

All India Peace and Solidarity Organisation -
West Bengal [AIPSO-WB] (WP), 5 Sarat
Ghosh Street (behind Entally Market),
Kolkota 700014 (bengalaipso@gmail.com)
(www.aipsowb.org).

Anuvrat Global Organisation [ANUVIBHA] (IB
EL ND PO CR), B01-02, Anuvibha Jaipur
Kendra, opp Gaurav Tower, Malviya Nagar
302017, Rajasthan (+91-141-404 9714)
(slgandhi@hotmail.com)
(www.anuvibha.in).

Atheist Centre (HR RA), Benz Circle,
Patamata, Vijayawada 520010, AP
(+91-866-247 2330) (fax 248 4850)
(atheistcentre@yahoo.com)
(www.atheistcentre.in).
Atheist.

Bombay Sarvodaya Friendship Centre (FR
WC SF), 701 Sainath Estate, Opp Lokmanya
Vidyalaya, Nilam Nagar-II, Mulund East,
Mumbai 400081 (+91-22-2563 1022)
(danielm@mtnl.net.in).

Centre for Peace and Development (AT ND
RE TW EL), 12/1 BT Rd "A" Cross,
Chamarajapet, Bangalore 560018
(+91-80-4153 8790).

Coalition for Nuclear Disarmament and Peace
[CNDP] (ND), A-124/6 - First Floor, Katwaria
Sarai, New Delhi 110016 (+91-11-6566 3958)
(fax 2651 7814) (cndpindia@gmail.com)
(www.cndpindia.com).
Network of 200 organisations.

Ekta Parishad (HR PO TW), Gandhi Bhawan,
Shyamla Hills, Bhopal, Madhya Pradesh
462002 (+91-755-422 3821) (fax)
(ektaparishad@yahoo.com)
(www.ektaparishad.org).
Federation of thousands of community
organisations.

Friends of the Gandhi Museum (RE EL PO),
B-4 Puru Society, Airport Rd, Lohegaon,
Pune 411032 (+91-937 120 1138)
(satyagrahi2000@gmail.com).

Gandhi Book Centre / Mumbai Sarvodaya
Mandal (PO), 299 Tardeo Rd, Nana Chowk,
Mumbai 400007 (+91-22-2387 2061)
(info@mkgandhi.org)
(www.mkgandhi.org).

Gandhi Research Foundation (RE), Gandhi
Teerth, Jain Hills PO Box 118, Jalgaon
425001, Maharashtra (+91-257-226 0011)
(fax 226 1133)
(gandhiexam@gandhifoundation.net)
(www.gandhifoundation.net).

INDIA

Greenpeace India (GP), 60 Wellington Rd, Richmond Town, Bangalore 560025, Karnataka (+91-80-2213 1899) (fax 4115 4862) (supporter.services.in@greenpeace.org) (www.greenpeace.org/india). Regional Office in Delhi (+91-11-6666 5000).

Gujarat Vidyapeeth (RE), Ashram Rd (near Income tax), Ahmedabad 380014 (+91-79-2754 0746) (fax 2754 2547) (registrar@gujaratvidyapith.org) (www.gujaratvidyapith.org). Gandhian study centre.

Indian Doctors for Peace and Development [IDPD] (IP), 139-E Kitchlu Nagar, Ludhiana 141001, Punjab (+91-161-230 4360) (fax 230 0252) (idpd2001@yahoo.com) (www.idpd.org).

Nagaland Peace Centre (PA CR), D Block, Kohima Town, PO Kohima 797001, Nagaland (+91-370-229 1400).

National Gandhi Museum and Library (RE), Rajghat, New Delhi 110002 (+91-11-2331 1793) (fax 2332 8310) (gandhimuseumdelhi@gmail.com) (www.gandhimuseum.org). Has collection of original relics, books, etc.

Organisation for Nuclear Disarmament, World Peace and Environment [ONADWPE] (ND EL), 11 Gautam Palli, Lucknow 226001, UP (+91-522-223 5659) (ammarrizvi505@yahoo.com).

Sikh Human Rights Group (South Asia) (HR CR), Chamber No 119, Ditrict Courts Sec 17, Chandigarh (shrgindia@shrg.net) (shrg.net).

Swadhina / Independence (WR), 34/C Bondel Rd, Ballygunge, Kolkata 700019 (+91-33-4001 0407) (mainoffice@swadhina.org.in) (www.swadhina.org.in).

Tibetan Centre for Human Rights and Democracy (FR HR), Narthang Building - Top Floor, Gangchen Kyishong, Dharamsala, HP 176215 (+91-1892-223363) (fax 225363) (office@tchrd.org) (www.tchrd.org). Works for human rights of Tibetans in Tibet.

War Resisters of India/West (WR), c/o Swati & Michael, Juna Mozda, Dediapada, Dt Narmada, Gujarat 393040 (+91-2649-290249) (mozdam@gmail.com).

Women's International League for Peace and Freedom - India [WILPF] (WL), c/o Peace Research Centre, Gujatat Vidyapith, Ahmedabad 380014.

IRAN

Iranian Physicians for Social Responsibility [PSR-Iran] (IP), PO Box 11155-18747, Tehran Peace Museum, Parke shahr, Tehran (+98-21-6675 6945) (fax 6693 9992) (info@irpsr.org).

Islamic Human Rights Commission [IHRC] (HR), PO Box 13165-137, Tehran (+98-21-8852 9742) (fax 8876 8807) (ihrc@ihrc.ir) (www.ihrc.ir).

IRELAND, NORTHERN

NOTE: Organisations working on an all-Ireland basis (ie covering both the Republic of Ireland and Northern Ireland), with their office address in the Irish Republic, will be found listed there. Similarly, groups operating on a United Kingdom-wide basis (ie covering both Britain and Northern Ireland), with a British-based office, will be found listed under Britain.

Amnesty International - NI Region [AI-NI] (AI), 397 Ormeau Rd, Belfast BT7 (+44-28-9064 3000) (fax 9069 0989) (nireland@amnesty.org.uk) (www.amnesty.org.uk/issues/Northern-Ireland).

Bahá'í Council for Northern Ireland (RP), Apt 4, 2 Lower Windsor Ave, Belfast BT9 (+44-28-9016 0457) (bcni@bahai.org.uk) (www.bahaicouncil-ni.org.uk).

Centre for Democracy and Peacebuilding (HR CR), 55 Knock Rd, Belfast BT5 (info@democracyandpeace.org) (democracyandpeace.org). Sharing peacebuilding expertise internationally.

Children are Unbeatable! Alliance (HR), Unit 9, 40 Montgomery Rd, Belfast BT6 (+44-28-9040 1290) (carolconlin@btinternet.com) (www.childrenareunbeatable.org.uk). For abolition of all physical punishment.

Christian Aid Ireland (TW), Linden House, Beechill Business Park, 96 Beechill Rd, Belfast BT8 7QN (+44-28-9064 8133) (belfast@christian-aid.org) (www.christianaid.ie).

Co-operation Ireland (CD), 5 Weavers Court Business Park, Linfield Rd, Belfast BT12 (+44-28-9032 1462) (info@cooperationireland.org) (www.cooperationireland.org). Works for tolerance and acceptance of differences.

Committee on the Administration of Justice [CAJ] (HR), Community House, Citylink Business Park, 6A Albert St, Belfast BT12 (+44-28-9031 6000) (fax 9031 4583) (info@caj.org.uk) (www.caj.org.uk). *Just News.*

Conflict Resolution and Reconciliation Studies Programme (RE CR RP), Irish School of Ecumenics (of Trinity College Dublin), 683 Antrim Rd, Belfast BT15 (+44-28-9077 5010) (fax 9037 3986) (reconsec@tcd.ie) (www.tcd.ie/ise). Research, teaching and outreach.

Corrymeela Community (RP), 83 University St, Belfast BT7 1HP (+44-28-9050 8080) (fax 9050 8070) (belfast@corrymeela.org) (www.corrymeela.org). *Corrymeela.*

Friends of the Earth - NI (FE), 7 Donegall Street Place, Belfast BT1 2FN (+44-28-9023 3488) (fax 9024 7556) (foe-ni@foe.co.uk) (www.foe.co.uk/ni).

Glebe House (CR), 23 Bishopscourt Rd, Kilclief, Strangford BT30, Co Down (+44-28-4488 1374) (info@glebehouseni.com)

Global Peacebuilders (CR), c/o Springboard Opportunities, 2nd Floor, 7 North St, Belfast BT1 1NH (+44-28-9031 5111) (fax 9031 3171) (james@springboard-opps.org) (www.globalpeacebuilders.org).

Green Party in Northern Ireland (EL), 1st Floor, 76 Abbey St, Bangor BT20 4JB (+44-28-9145 9110) (info@greenpartyni.org) (www.greenpartyni.org).

Healing Through Remembering [HTR] (RE), Alexander House, 17a Ormeau Ave, Belfast BT2 8HD (+44-28-9023 8844) (fax 9023 9944) (info@healingthroughremembering.org) (www.healingthroughremembering.org).

Institute for Conflict Research [ICR] (RE), North City Business Centre, 2 Duncairn Gdns, Belfast BT15 (+44-28-9074 2682) (fax 9035 6654) (info@conflictresearch.org.uk) (www.conflictresearch.org.uk).

Institute for the Study of Conflict Transformation and Social Justice [ISCTSJ] (RE CR), Queen's University Belfast, 19 University Sq, Belfast BT7 (+44-28-9097 3609) (ctsj@qub.ac.uk).

Irish Network for Nonviolent Action Training and Education [INNATE] (WR RA FR), c/o 16 Ravensdene Park, Belfast BT6 0DA (+44-28-9064 7106) (fax) (innate@ntlworld.com) (www.innatenonviolence.org). *Nonviolent News.*

Northern Ireland Community Relations Council [CRC] (CR PO RE), 2nd Floor, Equality House, 7-9 Shaftesbury Sq, Belfast BT2 7DP (+44-28-9022 7500) (info@nicrc.org.uk) (www.community-relations.org.uk).

Northern Ireland Council for Integrated Education [NICIE] (PO HR CD RE), 25 College Gdns, Belfast BT9 (+44-28-9097 2910) (fax 9097 2919) (info@nicie.org.uk) (www.nicie.org.uk).

Oxfam Ireland (TW), 115 North St, Belfast (+44-28-9023 0220) (fax 9023 7771) (info@oxfamireland.org) (www.oxfamireland.org).

Peace People (FR CD HR), 224 Lisburn Rd, Belfast BT9 6GE (+44-28-9066 3465) (info@peacepeople.com) (www.peacepeople.com).

Quaker Service (SF), 541 Lisburn Rd, Belfast BT9 7GQ (+44-28-9020 1444) (fax 9020 1881) (info@quakerservice.com) (www.quakerservice.com).

The Junction (CR PO), 8-14 Bishop St, Derry/Londonderry BT48 6PW (+44-28-7136 1942) (thejunction@thejunction-ni.org) (thejunction-ni.org). Community relations, civic empowerment.

TIDES Training (CR), 174 Trust, Duncairn Complex, Duncairn Ave, Belfast BT14 6BP (+44-28-9075 1686) (info@tidestraining.org) (www.tidestraining.org).

Tools for Solidarity - Ireland (TW PO), 55A Sunnyside St, Belfast BT7 (+44-28-9543 5972) (fax) (tools.belfast@myphone.coop) (www.toolsforsolidarity.com). *Solidarity.*

Transitional Justice Institute [TJI] (RE), Ulster University - Jordanstown Campus, Shore Rd, Newtownabbey BT37 (+44-28-9036 6202) (fax 9036 8962) (transitionaljustice@ulster.ac.uk) (www.transitionaljustice.ulster.ac.uk). Also Magee Campus, Londonderry.

IRELAND, REPUBLIC OF

Afri (IB HR TW AT), 134 Phibsborough Rd, Dublin 7 (+353-1-882 7581) (admin@afri.ie) (www.afri.ie). *Peacemaker.*

Amnesty International Ireland (AI), Sean MacBride House, 48 Fleet St, Dublin 2 (+353-1-863 8300) (fax 671 9338) (info@amnesty.ie) (www.amnesty.ie). *Amnesty Ireland.*

Chernobyl Children International (PO EL HR), 1A The Stables, Alfred St, Cork City (+353-21-455 8774) (fax 450 5564) (info@chernobyl-ireland.com) (www.chernobyl-international.com).

Co-operation Ireland (CI) (CD), Port Centre, Alexandra Rd, Dublin 1 (+353-1-819 7692) (fax 894 4962) (info@cooperationireland.org) (www.cooperationireland.org). Works for tolerance and acceptance of differences.

Comhlámh - Development Workers and Volunteers in Global Solidarity (TW HR), 12 Parliament St, Dublin 2 (+353-1-478 3490) (info@comhlamh.org) (www.comhlamh.org). Action and education for global justice.

Dóchas - The Irish Association of Non-Governmental Development Organisations (TW), 1-2 Baggot Court, Lower Baggot St, Dublin 2 (+353-1-405 3801) (fax 405 3802) (anna@dochas.ie) (www.dochas.ie).

Dublin Quaker Peace Committee (SF), c/o Quaker House, Stocking Lane, Rathfarnham, Dublin 16 (info@dublinquakerpeace.org) (www.dublinquakerpeace.org).

Educate Together (HR RE PO CR), 11-12 Hogan Place, Dublin 2 (+353-1-429 2500) (fax 429 2502) (info@educatetogether.ie) (www.educatetogether.ie).

Friends of the Irish Environment (EL), Kilcatherine, Eyeries, Co Cork (+353-27-74771) (admin@friendsoftheirishenvironment.org) (www.friendsoftheirishenvironment.org).

Green Party / Comhaontas Glas (EL AL RA HR), 16/17 Suffolk St, Dublin 2 (+353-1-679 0012) (fax 679 7168) (info@greenparty.ie) (www.greenparty.ie).

IRELAND, Republic

Irish Anti-War Movement, PO Box 9260, Dublin 1 (+353-1-872 7912) (info@irishantiwar.com) (www.irishantiwar.org).

Irish Campaign for Nuclear Disarmament / Feachtas um Dhí-armáil Eithneach [ICND] (IB ND), PO BOX 6327, Dublin 6 (irishcnd@gmail.com) (www.irishcnd.com). *Peacework.*

Irish Centre for Human Rights (HR), National University of Ireland, University Rd, Galway (+353-91-493948) (fax 494575) (humanrights@nuigalway.ie) (www.nuigalway.ie/human_rights).

Irish Peace Institute (RE CD PO), University of Limerick, Limerick (+353-61-202768) (fax 202572) (matthew.cannon@ul.ie) (www.ul.ie/ipi).

Irish United Nations Association [IUNA] (UN), 14 Lower Pembroke St, Dublin 2 (+353-1-661 6920) (irelandun@gmail.com).

Mediators' Institute Ireland [MII] (CR), Pavilion House, 31/32 Fitzwilliam Sq South, Dublin 2 (+353-1-609 9190) (fax 493 0595) (info@themii.ie) (www.themii.ie).

Pax Christi Ireland (PC HR AT), 52 Lower Rathmines Rd, Dublin 6 (+353-1-496 5293) (www.paxchristi.ie).

Peace and Neutrality Alliance / Comhaontas na Síochána is Neodrachta [PANA] (ND CD), 17 Castle St, Dalkey, Co Dublin (+353-1-235 1512) (info@pana.ie) (www.pana.ie).

Programme for International Peace Studies (RE), Irish School of Ecumenics - Loyola Institute Building, TCD - Main Campus, Dublin 2 (+353-1-896 4770) (fax 672 5024) (peacesec@tcd.ie) (www.tcd.ie/ise). *Unity.*

Servas (SE), c/o Donal Coleman, 53 Glengara Park, Glenageary, Co Dublin A96 TOF6 (+353-87-915 9635) (ireland@servas.org) (www.servas.org).

ShannonWatch (DA HR), PO Box 476, Limerick DSU, Dock Rd, Limerick (+353-87-822 5087) (shannonwatch@gmail.com) (www.shannonwatch.org). Monitors foreign military use of Shannon Airport.

Student Christian Movement (RP), 53 Clipper View, Ellis Quay, Dublin 7 (scmireland@gmail.com).

Vegetarian Society of Ireland [VSI] (EL PO), c/o Dublin Food Coop, 12 Newmarket, Dublin 8 (info@vegetarian.ie) (www.vegetarian.ie). *The Irish Vegetarian.*

Voluntary Service International [VSI] (SC), 30 Mountjoy Sq, Dublin 1 (+353-1-855 1011) (fax 855 1012) (info@vsi.ie) (www.vsi.ie). *VSI News.*

ISLE OF MAN

Shee Nish! / Peace Now! (AT PA DA), c/o Stuart Hartill, 1 The Sycamores, Walpole Rd, Ramsey IM8 1LU (+44-1624-814496) (stuarth@manx.net).
Widely-based coalition of peace campaigners.

ISRAEL (see also Palestine)

NOTE: Territories allocated to Israel in the United Nations partition of Palestine in 1947, together with further areas annexed by Israel prior to 1967, are included here. Other parts of Palestine occupied by Israel in 1967 or later are listed under Palestine.

Al-Beit - Association for the Defence of Human Rights in Israel (HR CD TW), PO Box 650, Arara 30026 (+972-6-635 4370) (fax 635 4367) (uridavis@actcom.co.il).
Concentrates on right of residence and housing.

Alternative Information Centre [AIC] (HR RE TW AL AT), POB 31417, West Jerusalem 91313 (+972-2-624 1159) (fax 3-762 4664) (connie.hackbarth@alternativenews.org) (www.alternativenews.org). *Economy of the Occupation.* See also Palestine.

Amnesty International Israel (AI), PO Box 5239, Tel-Aviv 66550 (+972-3-525 0005) (fax 525 0001) (info@amnesty.org.il) (amnesty.org.il).

Association for Civil Rights in Israel [ACRI] (HR), PO Box 34510, Jerusalem 91000 (+972-2-652 1218) (fax 652 1219) (mail@acri.org.il) (www.acri.org.il).

B'Tselem - Israeli Information Centre for Human Rights in the Occupied Territories (HR), PO Box 53132, West Jerusalem 9153002 (+972-2-673 5599) (fax 674 9111) (mail@btselem.org) (www.btselem.org).

Bimkom - Planners for Planning Rights (HR), 13 Ebenezra St - PO Box 7154, West Jerusalem 9107101 (+972-2-566 9655) (fax 566 0551) (bimkom@bimkom.org) (www.bimkom.org).

Coalition of Women for Peace [CWP] (HR CD), POB 29214, Tel Aviv - Jaffa 61292 (+972-3-528 1005) (fax) (cwp@coalitionofwomen.org) (www.coalitionofwomen.org).

Combatants for Peace (CD), PO Box 3049, Beit Yehushua 40591 (office@cfpeace.org) (www.cfpeace.org).
Israeli and Palestinian ex-fighters for peace.

Defence for Children International - Israel [DCI-Israel] (HR), PO Box 2533, West Jerusalem 91024 (+972-2-563 3003) (fax 563 1241) (dci@dci-il.org).

Givat Haviva Jewish-Arab Centre for Peace [JACP] (CR HR RE), MP Menashe 37850 (+972-4-630 9289) (fax 630 9305) (givathaviva@givathaviva.org.il) (www.givathaviva.org.il).

Greenpeace Mediterranean - Israel (GP HR), PO Box 20079, Tel Aviv 61200 (+972-3-561 4014) (fax 561 0415) (gpmedisr@greenpeace.org) (www.greenpeace.org/israel).

Gush Shalom / Peace Bloc (CD CR HR RE RA), PO Box 3322, Tel-Aviv 61033 (+972-3-522 1732) (fax 527 1108) (info@gush-shalom.org) (www.gush-shalom.org).

Hamerkaz Hamishpati L'zkhuyot Hami-ut Ha'aravi Beyisrael / Legal Centre for Arab Minority Rights in Israel [Adalah] (HR), 94 Yaffa St, PO Box 8921, Haifa 31090 (+972-4-950 1610) (fax 950 3140) (adalah@adalah.org) (www.adalah.org). Works for equal rights for Arab citizens in Israel.

Hand in Hand - Centre for Jewish-Arab Education in Israel (PO CD RE), PO Box 10339, Jerusalem 91102 (+972-2-673 5356) (info@handinhand.org.il) (www.handinhandk12.org). Supports integrated, bilingual education.

Igud Israeli Shel Rofim le Manat Milchamah Garinit / Physicians for Peace and Preservation of the Environment (IP EL RE), PO Box 19, Haparsa Rd, Kfar Yedidia 42940 (fridmanr@post.tau.ac.il).

Israel-Palestine Creative Regional Initiatives [IPCRI] (RE CR EL CD), see under Palestine (+972-52-238 1715) (www.ipcri.org).

Israeli Committee for a Middle East Free from Atomic, Biological and Chemical Weapons (ND RW), PO Box 16202, Tel Aviv 61161 (+972-3-522 2869) (fax) (spiro@bezeqint.net).

Mossawa Center - Advocacy Center for Arab Citizens in Israel (HR), 5 Saint Lucas St, PO Box 4471, Haifa 31043 (+972-4-855 5901) (fax 855 2772) (programs.mossawa@gmail.com) (www.mossawa.org).

New Profile - Movement to Demilitarise Israeli Society (WR), PO Box 3454, Ramat Hasharon 47100 (+972-3-516 0119) (info@newprofile.org) (www.newprofile.org). Feminist movement of women and men.

Ometz Le'sarev / Courage to Refuse, PO Box 16238, Tel Aviv (+972-3-523 3103) (info@seruv.org.il) (www.seruv.org.il). (Zionists) refusing deployment in the Territories.

OneVoice Movement - Israel [OVI] (CD CR), PO Box 29695, Tel Aviv 66881 (+972-3-516 8005) (info@OneVoice.org.il) (www.onevoicemovement.org). See also Palestine.

Palestinian-Israeli Peace NGO Forum (Israeli Office) (CD), c/o The Peres Center for Peace, 132 Kedem St, Jaffa 68066 (+972-3-568 0646) (fax 562 7265) (info@peres-center.org) (www.peacengo.org). See also under Palestine.

Parents' Circle - Families' Forum: Bereaved Israeli and Palestinian Families Supporting Peace and Tolerance (CD CR), 1 Hayasmin St, Ramat-Efal 52960 (+972-3-535 5089) (fax 635 8367) (contact@theparentscircle.com) (www.theparentscircle.com). See also under Palestine.

Public Committee Against Torture in Israel [PCATI] (HR), POB 4634, West Jerusalem 91046 (+972-2-642 9825) (fax 643 2847) (pcati@stoptorture.org.il) (www.stoptorture.org.il).

Rabbis for Human Rights [RHR] (HR), 9 HaRechavim St, West Jerusalem 9346209 (+972-2-648 2757) (fax 678 3611) (info@rhr.israel.net) (www.rhr.israel.net).

Sadaka-Reut - Arab-Jewish Partnership (CR RE HR CD), 35 Shivtey Israel St, PO Box 8523, Jaffa - Tel-Aviv 61084 (+972-3-518 2336) (fax) (info@reutsadaka.org) (www.reutsadaka.org).

Shalom Achshav / Peace Now, PO Box 22651, Tel Aviv 62032 (+972-3-602 3300) (fax 602 3301) (info@peacenow.org.il) (www.peacenow.org.il).

Shovrim Shtika / Breaking the Silence (HR), PO Box 51027, 6713206 Tel Aviv (info@breakingthesilence.org.il) (www.shovrimshtika.org). Also www.breakingthesilence.org.il.

Wahat al-Salam - Neve Shalom [WAS-NS] (HR RE CR PO CD), Doar Na / Mobile Post, Shimshon 9976100 (+972-2-999 6305) (fax 991 1072) (info@wasns.info) (wasns.org). "Oasis of Peace."

Windows - Israeli-Palestinian Friendship Centre (CD), PO Box 5195, Tel Aviv - Jaffa (+972-3-620 8324) (fax 629 2570) (office@win-peace.org) (www.win-peace.org). *Windows.* Chlenov 41. See also in Palestine.

ITALY

Amici Della Terra (FE), Via di Torre Argentina 18, 00186 Roma (+39-06 687 5308) (fax 06 6830 8610) (info@amicidellaterra.it) (www.amicidellaterra.it).

Amnesty International - Sezione Italiana (AI), Via G B de Rossi 10, 00161 Roma (+39-06 44901) (fax 06 449 0222) (info@amnesty.it) (www.amnesty.it).

Archivio Disarmo (IB RE AT), Piazza Cavour 17, 00193 Roma (+39-06 3600 0343) (fax 06 3600 0345) (info@archiviodisarmo.it) (www.archiviodisarmo.it). *Sistema Informativo a Schede.*

Associazione Italiana Medicina per la Prevenzione della Guerra Nucleare [AIMPGN] (IP), Via Bari 4, 64029 Silvi Marina (TE) (+39-085 935 1350) (fax 085 935 3333) (mdipaolantonio55@gmail.com) (www.ippnw-italy.org).

For explanation of codes and abbreviations, see introduction

ITALY

Associazione Memoria Condivisa (CR), Viale 1º Maggio 32, 71100 Foggia (+39-0881 637775) (fax) (info@memoriacondivisa.it) (www.memoriacondivisa.it).
Supports non-violence as a response to terrorism.

Associazione Obiettori Nonviolenti (PA), Via Giotto 28, 81100 Caserta (+39-0823 357791) (fax 0823 355167) (www.avvelenata.it/obiezione).

Associazione per la Pace (IB), Via Alessandro Cruto 43, 00146 Roma (assopace.nazionale@assopace.org) (www.assopace.org).

Associazione Volontari Obiettori Nonviolenti [AVOLON] (SC WR SD), Via E Scuri 1/c, 24128 Bergamo (+39-035 260073) (fax 035 403220) (info@avolon.it) (www.avolon.it).

Azione dei Cristiani per l'Abolizione della Tortura [ACAT] (HR), c/o Rinascita Cristiana, Via della Trasportina 15, 00193 Roma (+39-06 686 5358) (posta@acatitalia.it). (www.acatitalia.it).

Centro Studi Sereno Regis - Italian Peace Research Institute / Rete CCP [IPRI] (RE CR EL), Via Garibaldi 13, 10122 Torino (+39-011 532824) (fax 011 515 8000) (www.serenoregis.org). *IPRI Newsletter.*

CIPAX - Centro Interconfessionale per la Pace (RP TW CR EL), Via Ostiense 152/B, 00154 Roma (+39-06 5728 7347) (fax) (info@cipax-roma.it) (www.cipax-roma.it). *Strumenti di Pace.*

Eirene Centro studi per la pace (RE SD), Via Enrico Scuri 1, 24128 Bergamo (+39-035 260073) (fax 035 432 9224) (info@eirene.it) (www.eirene.it).

Gesellschaft für Bedrohte Völker / Associazione per i Popoli Minacciati / Lia por i Popui Manacês (HR), CP 233, 39100 Bozen/Bolzano, Südtirol (+39-0471 972240) (fax) (gfbv.bz@ines.org) (www.gfbv.it). Part of international GFBV network.

Green Cross Italy (EL TW DA HR), Via dei Gracchi 187, 00192 Roma (+39-06 3600 4300) (fax 06 3600 4364) (info@greencross.it) (www.greencrossitalia.org).

Greenpeace (GP), Via Della Cordonata 7, 00187 Roma (+39-06 6813 6061) (fax 06 4543 9793) (info.it@greenpeace.org) (www.greenpeace.org/italy). *GP News.*

International School on Disarmament and Research on Conflicts [ISODARCO] (RE CR DA), c/o Prof Carlo Schaerf, via della Rotonda 4, 00186 Roma (+39-06 689 2340) (isodarco@gmail.com) (www.isodarco.it).

Lega Internazionale delle Donne per la Pace e la Libertà [WILPF Italia] (WL), Via Misurina 69, 00135 Roma (+39-06 372 3742) (antonia.sani@alice.it) (wilpfitalia.wordpress.com).

Movimento Internazionale della Riconciliazione [MIR-MN] (FR), via Garibaldi 13, 10122 Torino (+39-011 532824) (fax 011 515 8000) (mir-mn.serenoregis.org).

Movimento Nonviolento [MN] (WR TR EL), Via Spagna 8, 37123 Verona (+39-045 800 9803) (fax) (azionenonviolenta@sis.it) (www.nonviolenti.org). *Azione Nonviolenta.*

Pax Christi Italia (PC), via Quintole per le Rose 131, 50029 Tavarnuzze, Firenze (+39-055 202 0375) (fax) (info@paxchristi.it) (www.paxchristi.it). *Mosaico di Pace.*

PBI Italia (PA RA HR), Via Asiago 5/a, 35010 Cadoneghe (PD) (info@pbi-italy.org) (www.pbi-italy.org).

Religioni per la Pace Italia (RP), Via Pio VIII 38-D-2, 00165 Roma (+39-333 273 1245) (info@religioniperlapaceitalia.org) (www.religioniperlapaceitalia.org).

Società Italiana per l'Organizzazione Internazionale [SIOI] (UN), Piazza di San Marco 51, 00186 Roma (+39-06 692 0781) (fax 06 678 9102) (sioi@sioi.org) (www.sioi.org). *La Comunità Internazionale.*

JAPAN

Chikyu no Tomo / Friends of the Earth (FE), 1-21-9 Komone, Itabashi-ku, Tokyo 173-0037 (+81-3-6909 5983) (fax 6909 5986) (info@foejapan.org) (www.foejapan.org).

Goi Peace Foundation / World Peace Prayer Society Japan Office (CD PO), Heiwa-Daiichi Bldg, 1-4-5 Hirakawa-Cho, Chiyoda-ku, Tokyo 102-0093 (+81-3-3265 2071) (fax 3239 0919) (info@goipeace.or.jp) (www.goipeace.or.jp).

Green Action (EL), Suite 103, 22-75 Tanaka Sekiden-cho, Sakyo-ku, Kyoto 606-8203 (+81-75-701 7223) (fax 702 1952) (info@greenaction-japan.org) (www.greenaction-japan.org). Campaigns especially against nuclear fuel cycle.

Greenpeace Japan (GP), N F Bldg 2F 8-13-11, Nishi-Shinjuku, Shinjuku, Tokyo 160-0023 (+81-3-5338 9800) (fax 5338 9817) (www.greenpeace.or.jp).

Hiroshima Peace Culture Foundation [HPCF] (PA ND RE), 1-2 Nakajima-cho, Naka-ku, Hiroshima 730-0811 (+81-82-241 5246) (fax 542 7941) (p-soumu@pcf.city.hiroshima.jp) (www.pcf.city.hiroshima.jp/hpcf). *Peace Culture.*

Hiroshima Peace Memorial Museum (RE), 1-2 Nakajima-cho, Naka-ku, Hiroshima 730-0811 (+81-82-241 4004) (fax 542 7941) (hpcf@pcf.city.hiroshima.jp) (www.pcf.city.hiroshima.jp).

Japan Council Against A & H Bombs - Gensuikyo (IB ND PA), 2-4-4 Yushima, Bunkyo-ku, Tokyo 113-8464 (+81-3-5842 6034) (fax 5842 6033) (antiatom@topaz.plala.or.jp) (www.antiatom.org). *No More Hiroshimas*; *Gensuikyo Tsushin*. National federation.

Japanese Physicians for the Prevention of Nuclear War [JPPNW] (IP), c/o Hiroshima Prefectural Medical Association, 3-2-3 Futabanosato, Higashi-ku, Hiroshima 732-0057 (+81-82-568 1511) (fax 568 2112) (ippnw-japan@hiroshima.med.or.jp) (www.hiroshima.med.or.jp).

Kyoto Museum for World Peace (RE), Ritsumeikan University, 56-1 Kitamachi, Toji-in, Kyoto 603-8577 (+81-75-465 8151) (fax 465 7899) (peacelib@st.ritsumei.ac.jp) (www.ritsumei.ac.jp/mng/er/wp-museum).

Nihon Hidankyo / Japan Confederation of A- and H-Bomb Sufferers' Organisations (ND CR HR), Gable Bldg 902, 1-3-5 Shiba Daimon, Minato-ku, Tokyo 105-0012 (+81-3-3438 1897) (fax 3431 2113) (kj3t-tnk@asahi-net.or.jp) (www.ne.jp/asahi/hidankyo/nihon). *Hidankyo.*

Organising Committee - World Conference Against A and H bombs (ND), 2-4-4 Yushima, Bunkyo-ku, Tokyo 113-8464 (+81-3-5842 6034) (fax 5842 6033) (intl@antiatom.org).

Peace Depot - Peace Resources Cooperative (ND PA RE), Hiyoshi Gruene 1st Floor, 1-30-27-4 Hiyoshi Hon-cho, Kohoku-ku, Yokohama 223-0062 (+81-45-563 5101) (fax 563 9907) (office@peacedepot.org) (www.peacedepot.org). *Nuclear Weapon & Nuclear Test Monitor.*

Peace Promotion Division of the City of Hiroshima (ND CD), 1-5 Nakajima-cho, Naka-ku, Hiroshima 730-0811 (+81-82-242 7831) (fax 242 7452) (peace@city.hiroshima.jp).

Toda Peace Institute (RE CR PA WF ND), 15-3 Samon-cho, Shinjuku-ku, Tokyo 160-0017 (contact@toda.org) (www.toda.org).

United Nations Association (UN), Nippon Building - Rm 427, 2-6-2 Ohtemachi, Chiyoda-ku, Tokyo 100-8699 (+81-3-3270 4731) (info@unaj.or.jp) (www.unaj.or.jp).

KENYA

African Great Lakes Initiative of the Friends Peace Teams [AGLI] (SF CR), PO Box 189, Kipkarren River 50241 (+254-726-790783) (Dave@aglifpt.org) (www.aglifpt.org). US Office: +1-314-647 1287.

Centre for Research and Dialogue - Somalia [CRD] (CR RE), PO Box 28832, Nairobi (www.crdsomalia.org). Based in Mogadishu, Somalia.

Life & Peace Institute - Somalia and Kenya Programme (RP CR), AACC Commercial Building - 5th floor, off Waiyaki Way, Nairobi (+254-20-444 0431) (fax 444 0433) (michele.cesari@life-peace.org) (www.life-peace.org).

Sudanese Women's Voice for Peace, PO Box 21123, Nairobi.

KOREA, REPUBLIC OF

Greenpeace East Asia - Seoul Office (GP), 2/F - 358-121 Seogyo-dong, Mapo-gu, Seoul (+82-2-3144 1994) (fax 6455 1995) (greenpeace.kr@greenpeace.org) (www.greenpeace.org/eastasia).

International Peace Youth Group [IPYG] (RP), 201 Daeseong Building, Gaepodong, Gangnam-gu 1230-9, Seoul 135892 (admin@ipyg.org) (ipyg.org).

Korea Federation for Environmental Movement [KFEM] (FE), 251 Nooha-dong, Jongno-gu, Seoul 110-806 (+82-2-735 7000) (fax 730 1240) (ma@kfem.or.kr) (www.kfem.or.kr). Anti-nuclear movement.

Pyeonghwa wa Tongil Yoneun Saramdeul / Solidarity for Peace and Re-Unification of Korea [SPARK] (PC), 3-47 Beonji 2 Cheung, Chungjeongno 3 ga, Sodaemun-gu, Seoul 120-837 (+82-2-711 7292) (fax 712 8445) (spark946@hanmail.net) (www.peaceone.org). *Pyeonghwamuri.*

LATVIA

Vides Aizsardzibas Klubs / Environment Protection Club [VAK] (FE), 11 Novembra Krastmala - 35 - 104 istaba, 1966 Riga (+371-6722 6042) (info@vak.lv) (www.vak.lv).

LEBANON

Greenpeace Mediterranean (GP), PO Box 13-6590, Beirut (+961-1-361255) (fax 36 1254) (supporters@greenpeace.org.lb) (www.greenpeace.org/lebanon). See also Israel, Turkey.

Lebanon Conflict Resolution Network [LCRN] (CR), PO Box 55215, Vanlian Centre, Sin-al-Fil, Beirut (+961-1-486430) (fax 490375) (armenb@lcps-lebanon.org).

Resource Centre for Gender Equality [ABAAD] (HR), PO Box 50-048, Beirut (+961-1-283820) (fax 283821) (abaad@abaadmena.org) (www.abaadmena.org).

WILPF (WL), c/o Nouha Ghosn, PO Box 14-6725, Beirut.

LITHUANIA

United Nations Association (UN HR), Lithuanian Culture Research Institute, Saltoniskiu St 58, 08015 Vilnius (+370-5-275 1898) (jurate128@yahoo.de).

LUXEMBOURG

Action des Chrétiens pour l'Abolition de la Torture [ACAT] (HR), 5 Av Marie-Thérèse, 2132 Luxembourg (+352-4474 3558) (fax 4474 3559) (contact@acat.lu) (www.acat.lu).

Association Luxembourgeoise pour les Nations Unies [ALNU] (UN), 3 Rte d'Arlon, 8009 Strassen (+352-461468) (fax 461469) (alnu@pt.lu) (www.alnu.lu).

Déi Gréng (EL PA), 3 rue du Fosssé, 1536 Luxembourg (+352-274 8271) (fax 2748 2722) (greng@greng.lu) (www.greng.lu). Green Party.

LUXEMBOURG

Greenpeace Luxembourg (GP), BP 229, 4003 Esch/Alzette (+352-546 2521) (fax 545405) (membres.lu@greenpea.org) (www.greenpeace.org/luxembourg).
Iwerliewen fir Bedreete Volleker (HR), BP 98, 6905 Niederanven (+352-2625 8687) (info@iwerliewen.org) (iwerliewen.org).
Servas (SE), see under Belgium.

MACEDONIA

Dvizenje na ekologistitje na Makedonija / Ecologists' Movement of Macedonia [DEM] (FE), Vasil Gjorgjov Street 36 - baraka 6, 1000 Skopje (+389-2-220518) (fax) (dem@dem.org.mk) (www.dem.org.mk).
Nansen Dialogue Centre Skopje [NDC Skopje] (CR CD), Str Bahar Mois No 4, 1000 Skopje (+389-2-320 9905) (fax 320 9906) (ndcskopje@nansen-dialogue.net) (ndc.net.mk).
United Nations Association of Macedonia (UN), St Zorz Bize 9-b, 1000 Skopje (+389-2-244 3751) (fpesevi@mt.net.mk) (www.sunamk.org).

MADAGASCAR

FIEFA - Fikambanana Entaninny Fihavanana eto Madagasikara [MIR-MAD] (FR), BP 3763, Antananarivo 101 (+261-20 224 1771) (fax 20 224 1734) (fiefa@blueline.mg).

MALAWI

Citizens for Justice - Friends of the Earth Malawi (FE), Post Dot Net, Box X100, Crossroads, Lilongwe (+265-176 1887) (fax 176 1886) (info@cfjmalawi.org) (cfjmalawi.org).

MALAYSIA

Sahabat Alam Malaysia / Friends of the Earth Malaysia [SAM] (FE), 258 Jalan Air Itam, George Town, 10460 Penang (+60-4-228 6930) (fax 228 6932) (sam_inquiry@yahoo.com) (www.foe-malaysia.org).
United Nations Association Malaysia (UN), c/o YM Tengku Rithauddeen's Office, Level 3A, Holiday Villa Subang Jaya No 9, Jalan SS 12/1, 47500 Selangor (+60-3-5631 1186) (fax 5631 9399) (info@unam.org.my) (unam.org.my).

MALTA

John XXIII Peace Laboratory [Peacelab] (IB RP RE), Triq Hal-Far, Zurrieq ZRQ 2609 (+356-2168 9504) (fax 2164 1591) (info@peacelab.org) (www.peacelab.org). It-Tieqa.

MAURITIUS

Lalit (SF WL PA), 153 Main Rd, GRNW, Port-Louis (+230-208 5551) (lalitmail@intnet.mu) (www.lalitmauritius.org). Revi Lalit de Klas. Anti-militarist party and campaign.

MEXICO

Greenpeace Mexico (GP), Santa Margarita 227, Col del Valle, 03100 México DF (+52-55-5687 9595) (fax 5687 9030) (greenpeace.mexico@greenpeace.org) (www.greenpeace.org/mexico).
Médicos Mexicanos para la Prevención de la Guerra Nuclear (IP), Antiguo Claustro - Hospital Juarez - PA, Plaza San Pablo, 06090 Mexico - DF (fromow@servidor.unam.mx).
Servicio Paz y Justicia - México [SERPAJ] (RP), AP 4-80, 62431 Cuernavaca - Morelos (serpajc@laneta.apc.org).

MONACO

Organisation pour la Paix par le Sport - Peace and Sport (CD), Immeuble les Mandariniers, 42ter Blvd du Jardin Exotique, 98000 (+377-9797 7800) (fax 9797 1891) (contact@peace-sport.org) (www.peace-sport.org).

MONGOLIA

Oyu Tolgoi Watch (EL HR), POB 636, Ulaanbaatar 46A (+976-9918 5828) (otwatch@gmail.com). Opposing devastation by Rio Tinto mining project.

MONTENEGRO

Nansen Dialogue Centre Montenegro (CR CD), Cetinsjki put bb 16/2, 81000 Podgorica (+382-20-290094) (fax) (ndcmontenegro@nansen-dialogue.net) (nansen-dialogue.net/ndcmontenegro).

MOZAMBIQUE

Justiça Ambiental / Friends of the Earth Mozambique [JA] (FE), Rua Marconi 110 - 1 andar, Maputo (+258-21 496668) (fax) (ja-ngo@tdm.co.mz) (ja4change.wordpress.com).

NAMIBIA

Earthlife Namibia (ELA) (EL), PO Box 24892, Windhoek (+264-61-227913) (fax 305213) (earthl@iway.na).

NEPAL

Amnesty International Nepal (AI), PO Box 135, Basanta Nagar, Belaju, Kathmandu (+977-1-436 4706) (fax 435 4987) (info@amnestynepal.org) (www.amnestynepal.org).
Ban Landmines Campaign Nepal [NCBL] (AT), Sitapaila, Ring Road, PO Box 5840, Kathmandu (+977-1-427 7428) (ncbl@mail.com.np) (nepal.icbl.org).
Concern for Children and Environment - Nepal [CONCERN] (EL HR CR), Dallu Aawas, PO Box 4543, Kathmandu (+977-1-428 8253) (fax 427 7033) (concern@mos.com.np) (concern.org.np).

For explanation of codes and abbreviations, see introduction

Human Rights and Peace Foundation [HURPEF] (HR), GPO 8975, Epc 5397, Kathmandu (+977-1-438 5231) (hurpef@hons.com.np) (www.hurpef.org.np).

Nepal Physicians for Social Responsibility (IP), PO Box 19624, Bagbazar, Kathmandu (psrn@healthnet.org.np).

People's Forum for Human Rights - Bhutan (HR), Anarmani 4, Birtamod, Jhapa (+977-23-540824) (rizal_pfhrb@ntc.net.np).

NETHERLANDS

Anti-Militaristies Onderzoekskollectief - VD AMOK (PA RE AT ND), Lauwerecht 55, 3515 GN Utrecht (+31-30-890 1341) (kees@amok.antenna.nl) (www.vdamok.nl).

Campagne tegen Wapenhandel (AT), Anna Spenglerstr 71, 1054 NH Amsterdam (+31-20-616 4684) (fax) (info@stopwapenhandel.org) (www.stopwapenhandel.org). *Campaign against arms trade.*

Centre for International Conflict Analysis and Management [CICAM] (RE), Postbus 9108, 6500 HK Nijmegen (+31-24-361 5687) (cicam@fm.ru.nl) (www.ru.nl/cicam).

Christian Peacemaker Teams - Nederland [CPT-NL] (RP RA PA), c/o Irene van Setten, Bredasingel 70, 6843 RE Arnhem (+31-26-848 1706) (info@cpt-nl.org) (www.cpt-nl.org).

Greenpeace Nederland (GP), NDSM-Plein 32, 1033 WB Amsterdam (+31-20-626 1877) (fax 622 1272) (info@greenpeace.nl) (www.greenpeace.nl).

GroenFront! (EL RA), Postbus 85069, 3508 AB Utrecht (info@groenfront.nl) (www.groenfront.nl). *Frontnieuws. Earth First!-style group.*

Kerk en Vrede (FR PA RE), Obrechtstr 43, 3572 EC Utrecht (+31-30-231 6666) (secretariaat@kerkenvrede.nl) (kerkenvrede.nl).

Museum voor Vrede en Geweldloosheid [MVG] (RE PA), Vlamingstr 82, 2611 DA Delft (+31-15-785 0137) (info@vredesmuseum.nl) (www.vredesmuseum.nl). *De Vredesboot.*

Musicians without Borders (RP), Kloveniersburgwal 87, 1011 KA Amsterdam (+31-20-330 5012) (info@musicianswithoutborders.org) (www.musicianswithoutborders.org).

Nederlands Expertisecentrum Alternatieven voor Geweld / Netherlands Expertise Centre Alternatives to Violence [NEAG] (CR), Vossiusstr 20, 1071 AD Amsterdam (+31-20-670 5295) (info@neag.nl) (www.neag.nl). *Affiliated to Nonviolent Peaceforce.*

Pax (PA CT AT RE CD), Postbus 19318, 3501 DH Utrecht (+31-30-233 3346) (fax 236 8199) (info@paxvoorvrede.nl) (www.paxvoorvrede.nl). *Formerly IKV Pax Christi. Also www.paxforpeace.nl.*

Peace Brigades International - Afdeling Nederland [PBI] (RA PO CR RE), Oudegracht 36, 3511 AP Utrecht (info@peacebrigades.nl) (www.peacebrigades.nl).

Ploughshares Support Group / Amsterdamse Catholic Worker (PA AT RP HR), Postbus 12622, 1100 AP Amsterdam (+31-20-699 8996) (noelhuis@antenna.nl) (noelhuis.nl). *Nieuwsbrief Jeannette Noelhuis.*

Religieus Genootschap der Vrienden - Quakers Nederland (SF), Postbus 2167, 7420 AD Deventer (+31-570-655229) (secretariaat@dequakers.nl) (www.quakers.nu). *De Vriendenkring.*

Stichting Voor Aktieve Geweldloosheid [SVAG] (SD PO RE), Postbus 288, 5280 AG Boxtel (info@geweldloosactief.nl) (www.geweldlozekracht.nl). *Geweldloze Kracht.*

Stichting Vredesburo Eindhoven (PA RE), Grote Berg 41, 5611 KH Eindhoven (+31-40-244 4707) (fax) (info@vredesburo.nl) (www.vredesburo.nl). *Vredesburo Nieuwsbrief.*

Upact (PO RE), Postbus 19, 3500 AA Utrecht (+31-30-223 8724) (info@upact.nl) (www.upact.nl). *Upact Nieuws.*

Vereniging Milieudefensie (FE), Postbus 19199, 1000 GD Amsterdam (+31-20-550 7300) (fax 550 7310) (service@milieudefensie.nl) (www.milieudefensie.nl). *Down to Earth.*

Vredesbeweging Pais (WR EL), Vlamingstr 82, 2611 LA Delft (+31-15-785 0137) (info@vredesbeweging.nl) (www.vredesbeweging.nl). *vredesmagazine.*

Vrijwillige Internationale Aktie [VIA] (SC), M v B Bastiaansestra 56, 1054 SP Amsterdam (info@stichtingvia.nl) (www.stichtingvia.nl).

Vrouwen en Duurzame Vrede (CR ND SD), Haaksbergerstr 317, 7545 GJ Enschede (+31-53-434 0559) (info@vrouwenenduurzamevrede.nl) (www.vrouwenenduurzamevrede.nl).

Women Peacemakers Program [WPP] (WR CD), Laan van Meerdervoort 70, 2517 AN Den Haag (+31-70-345 2671) (info@womenpeacemakersprogram.org) (www.womenpeacemakersprogram.org). *Cross the Lines. Formerly Women Peacemakers Programme of IFOR.*

Women's International League for Peace and Freedom - Netherlands [WILPF-IVVV] (WL), Laan van Nieuw Oost Indië 252, 2593 CD Den Haag (+31-345-615105) (info@wilpf.nl) (www.wilpf.nl).

NEW ZEALAND / AOTEAROA

Abolition 2000 Aotearoa New Zealand [A2000 ANZ] (ND), c/o Pax Christi, PO Box 68419, Newton, Aukland 1145 (+64-9-377 5541) (abolition2000@ymail.com) (www.a2000.org.nz).

NEW ZEALAND

Amnesty International (AI), PO Box 5300, Wellesley St, Auckland 1141 (+64-9-303 4520) (fax 303 4528) (info@amnesty.org.nz) (www.amnesty.org.nz).

Anabaptist Association of Australia and New Zealand (RP), see under Australia.

Anglican Pacifist Fellowship [APF] (RP AT TR), c/o Indrea Alexander, 9 Holmes St, Waimate 7924 (apfnzsecretary@gmail.com) (converge.org.nz/pma/apf). *The Anglican Pacifist of Aotearoa New Zealand.*

Anti-Bases Campaign [ABC] (PA RE), Box 2258, Christchurch 8140 (abc@chch.planet.org.nz) (www.converge.org.nz/abc). 2 yrly.

Campaign Against Foreign Control of Aotearoa [CAFCA], PO Box 2258, Christchurch 8140 (cafca@chch.planet.org.nz) (www.cafca.org.nz). *Foreign Control Watchdog.*

Catholic Worker (RP), PO Box 33-135, Christchurch (+64-3-338 7105) (www.catholicworker.org.nz).

Disarmament and Security Centre [DSC] (IB WL RE ND CR), PO Box 8390, Christchurch 8440 (+64-3-348 1353) (fax) (kate@chch.planet.org.nz) (www.disarmsecure.org).

Engineers for Social Responsibility [ESR] (EL ND AT), PO Box 6208, Wellesley Street, Auckland 1141 (www.esr.org.nz).

Green Party of Aotearoa/NZ (EL), PO Box 11652, Wellington 6142 (+64-4-801 5102) (fax 801 5104) (greenparty@greens.org.nz) (www.greens.org.nz). *Te Awa.*

Greenpeace Aotearoa New Zealand (GP), 11 Akiraho St, Mount Eden, Auckland (+64-9-630 6317) (fax 630 7121) (info@greenpeace.org.nz) (www.greenpeace.org/new-zealand).

IPPNW New Zealand (IP), PO Box 1702, Wellington 6140 (nwilson@actrix.gen.nz) (ippnw.org.nz).

New Zealand Burma Support Group (HR EL), 14 Waitati Pl, Mt Albert, Auckland (+64-9-828 4855) (nzburma@xtra.co.nz). *Newsletter.*

New Zealand Campaign Against Land Mines [CALM] (AT), PO Box 11504, Wellington 6004 (+64-21-996905) (nathan@boost.co.nz) (calm.org.nz). Network of groups.

Pax Christi Aotearoa/NZ (PC), PO Box 68419, Newton, Aukland (paxnz@xtra.co.nz) (nzpaxchristi.wordpress.com).

Peace Action Wellington (DA AT RA), PO Box 9263, Wellington (peacewellington@riseup.net) (peacewellington.org). Work includes direct action against arms fairs.

Peace Council of Aotearoa/New Zealand [PCANZ] (WP), 13 Bell St, Otaki 5512 (+64-6-364 8940) (fax) (bt.richards@xtra.co.nz).

Peace Foundation (CR RE), PO Box 8055, Symonds Street, Auckland 1150 (+64-9-373 2379) (fax 379 2668) (peace@peacefoundation.org.nz) (kiaora.peace.net.nz).

Peace Movement Aotearoa [PMA] (AT HR PA RE), PO Box 9314, Wellington 6141 (+64-4-382 8129) (fax 382 8173) (pma@xtra.co.nz) (www.converge.org.nz/pma). National networking body.

Quaker Peace and Service Aotearoa/New Zealand [QPSANZ] (SF), Quaker Meeting House, 72 Cresswell Ave, Christchurch 8061 (+64-3-980 4884) (www.quaker.org.nz/groups/qpsanz).

Stop the Arms Trade NZ (AT DA), PO Box 9843, Wellington (stop-the-arms-trade@riseup.net) (www.stopthearmstrade.nz). Actions against weapons expos.

United Nations Association of New Zealand [UNANZ] (UN), PO Box 24494, Wellington 6142 (+64-4-496 9638) (office@unanz.org.nz) (unanz.org.nz).

Women's International League for Peace and Freedom [WILPF] (WL), PO Box 2054, Wellington (wilpfaotearoa@gmail.com) (www.wilpf.org.nz).

NICARAGUA

Centro de Prevención de la Violencia [CEPREV] (HR PO DA), Villa Fontana - casa 23, Club Terraza 1/2 c al lago, Managua (fax +505-2278 1637) (www.ceprev.org). Promotes a culture of peace.

Red de Mujeres Contra la Violencia (HR PO RE), Aptdo 5965, Managua (+505-2266 4619) (www.reddemujerescontralaviolencia.org.ni).

NIGERIA

Carefronting Nigeria - Alternatives to Violence Project [AVP Nigeria] (WR), PO Box 1499, Kaduna (carefronting@yahoo.com) (www.carefronting.org).

Civil Liberties Organisation of Nigeria [CLO] (HR), 13 Soji Adepegba Close, off Allen Avenue, Ikeja, Lagos (clonigeria.org).

Pan-African Reconciliation Centre [PARC] (IB FR RE), PO Box 9354, Marina, Lagos City 101001 (+234-805-400 3843) (afropax@gmail.com) (www.parc-journal.webs.com).

Peace Initiative Network [PIN] (CR CD RE), PO Box 14937, Kano (+234-64-316663) (info@peaceinitiativenetwork.org) (www.peaceinitiativenetwork.org).

United Nations Association (UN), PO Box 54423, Falomo, Ikoyi, Lagos (+234-1-269 3112) (fax).

NORWAY

Amnesty International (AI), PO Box 702, Sentrum, 0106 Oslo (+47-2240 2200) (fax 2240 2250) (info@amnesty.no) (www.amnesty.no).

Folkereisning Mot Krig [FMK] (WR AT), PO Box 2779, Solli, 0204 Oslo (+47-2246 4670) (fax) (fmk@ikkevold.no) (www.ikkevold.no). *Ikkevold.*

Fred og Forsoning - IFOR Norge (FR), Fredshuset, Møllergata 12, 0179 Oslo (contact@ifor.no) (www.ifor.no).

Greenpeace Norge (GP), Pb 33, Torshov, 0412 Oslo (+47-2220 5101) (info.no@greenpeace.no) (www.greenpeace.no/norway).

Informasjonsarbeidere for Fred [IF] (IB AT ND DA), c/o Heffermehl, Stensgaten 24B, 0358 Oslo (+47-9174 4783) (fredpax@online.no) (peaceispossible.info).

Internasjonal Dugnad [ID] (SC), Nordahl Brunsgt 22, 0165 Oslo (+47-2211 3123) (info@internasjonaldugnad.org) (www.internasjonaldugnad.org). *Dugnad Nytt.*

Miljøpartiet De Grønne [MDG] (EL HR PA), Hausmanns gate 19, 0182 Oslo (+47-2369 9411) (mdg@mdg.no) (www.mdg.no).

Narviksenteret - Nordnorsk Fredssenter (IB), Postboks 700, 8509 Narvik (+47-9154 7078) (fax 7694 4560) (fred.no).

Nei til Atomvåpen / No to Nuclear Weapons (ND), Postboks 8838, Youngstorget, 0028 Oslo (post@neitilatomvapen.org) (www.neitilatomvapen.no).

Nobels Fredssenter / Nobel Peace Centre (RE), PO Box 1894 Vika, 0124 Oslo (+47-4830 1000) (fax 9142 9238) (post@nobelpeacecenter.org) (www.nobelpeacecenter.org).

Norges Fredslag (DA AT ND RE), Grensen 9B, Postboks 8922, Youngstorget, 0028 Oslo (www.fredslaget.no). Norwegian Peace Association.

Norges Fredsråd / Norwegian Peace Council (IB), Postboks 8940 Youngstorget, 0028 Oslo (+47-9527 4822) (fax 2286 8401) (post@norgesfredsrad.no) (norgesfredsrad.no)

Norwegian Nobel Institute / Det Norske Nobelinstitutt (RE DA CR), Henrik Ibsens gate 51, 0255 Oslo (+47-2212 9300) (fax 9476 1117) (postmaster@nobel.no) (nobelpeaceprize.org)

PBI-Norge (CR HR PA), Postboks 1742 Vika, 0121 Oslo (+47-9587 7117) (kontakt@pbi.no) (www.pbi.no).

Vennenes Samfunn Kvekerne i Norge (SF TR), Sandvigå 27 (2 etasje), 4007 Stavanger (+47-5152 9628) (fax 5152 5832) (Oslomm@kveker.org) (www.kveker.org).

WILPF Norge - Internasjonal Kvinneliga for Fred og Frihet [IKFF] (WL), Storgata 11, 0155 Oslo (+47-9308 9644) (ikff@ikff.no) (www.ikff.no). *Fred og Frihet.*

PAKISTAN

Human Rights Commission of Pakistan [HRCP] (HR), Aiwan-i-Jamhoor, 107 Tipu Block, New Garden Town, Lahore 54600 (+92-42-3586 4994) (fax 3588 3582) (hrcp@hrcp-web.org) (www.hrcp-web.org).

National Justice and Peace Commission (PC), E-64/A - Street 8, Officers Colony, Walton Rd, Lahore (+92-42-666 8692) (fax 665 5549) (ncjppakistan@gmail.com).

Revolutionary Association of the Women of Afghanistan [RAWA] (HR), PO Box 374, Quetta (+92-300-554 1258) (fax +44-870-8312326) (rawa@rawa.org) (www.rawa.org).

Servas Pakistan [SE-PK] (SE), c/o Muhammad Naseem, GPO Box 516, Lahore 54000 (+92-321-444 4516) (fax 42-3532 2223) (servaspakistan@yahoo.com) (pages.intnet.mu/servas/Pakistan). *Servas Pakistan Newsletter.*

Women's Internationl League for Peace and Freedom (WL), Sharah-e-Kashmir, Gulab Nagar, nr Darbar Saeen Mircho, Sector H-13, Islamabad (+92-51-250 6521) (mossarat_coco@yahoo.com).

PALESTINE (see also Israel)

NOTE: Because all of Palestine is under Israeli control (including areas not under day-to-day occupation), it is advisable to add 'via Israel' to addresses here (as well as 'Palestine').

Al-Watan Centre (CR HR RE), PO Box 158, Hebron, West Bank (+970-2-222 3777) (fax 222 0907) (info@alwatan.org) (www.alwatan.org). Supports popular resistance and nonviolence.

Alternative Information Centre [AIC] (HR RE TW AL AT), Building 111, Main Street, Beit Sahour, West Bank (+972-2-277 5444) (fax 277 5445) (www.alternativenews.org). See also Israel.

Centre for Conflict Resolution and Reconciliation [CCRR] (FR PC CR CD), PO Box 861, Bethlehem, West Bank (+970-2-276 7745) (fax 274 5475) (ccrr@ccrr-pal.org) (www.ccrr-pal.org). *Tree of Hope.*

Christian Peacemaker Teams [CPT] (RP), c/o Redeemer Church, PO Box 14076, Muristan Rd, Jerusalem 91140 (+972-2-292 8485) (cptheb@cpt.org) (www.cpt.org).

Combatants for Peace (CD), Ramallah (for postal address, see under Israel) (office@cfpeace.org) (www.cfpeace.org). Palestinian and Israeli ex-fighters for peace.

Defence for Children International - Palestine Section [DCI] (HR), PO Box 55201, East Jerusalem (+972-2-242 7530) (fax 242 7018) (rifat.kassis@dci-pal.org) (www.dci-palestine.org).

Ecumenical Accompaniment Programme in Palestine and Israel - Jerusalem Office [EAPPI] (RP HR CD CR), PO Box 741, East Jerusalem 91000 (+972-2-628 9402) (communications@eappi.org) (eappi.org).

PALESTINE

Holy Land Trust [HLT] (CR PO HR), PO Box 737, Bethlehem, West Bank (+972-2-276 5930) (fax 276 5931) (palestine@holylandtrust.org) (www.holylandtrust.org). Promotes nonviolent resistance to the occupation.

International Peace and Co-operation Centre [IPCC] (TW CR), PO Box 24162, Jerusalem 91240 (+972-2-581 1992) (fax 540 0522) (info@ipcc-jerusalem.org) (home.ipcc-jerusalem.org).

Israel-Palestine Creative Regional Initiatives [IPCRI] (RE CR EL CD), PO Box 11091, Jerusalem 91110 (+972-2-676 9460) (fax 676 8011) (ipcri@ipcri.org) (www.ipcri.org).
Office is in Ammunition Hill, East Jerusalem.

Jerusalem Center for Women (HR), PO Box 21929, East Jerusalem 51630 (+972-2-656 8532) (fax 656 8291) (info@j-c-w.org) (www.j-c-w.org).

Movement Against Israeli Apartheid in Palestine [MAIAP] (HR), see under Israel.

OneVoice Movement - Palestine (CD CR), PO Box 2401, Ramallah, West Bank (+970-2-295 2076) (info@OneVoice.ps) (www.onevoicemovement.org).
See also Israel.

Palestinian Campaign for the Academic and Cultural Boycott of Israel [PACBI], PO Box 1701, Ramallah (pacbi@pacbi.org) (www.pacbi.org). *Risala.*

Palestinian Centre for Human Rights [PCHR] (HR), PO Box 1328, Gaza City, Gaza Strip (+970-8-282 4776) (fax) (pchr@pchrgaza.org) (www.pchrgaza.org).

Palestinian Human Rights Monitoring Group [PHRMG] (HR), PO Box 19918, East Jerusalem 91198 (+972-2-583 8189) (fax 583 7197) (admin@phrmg.org) (www.phrmg.org). Office: Ahmad Jaber House, Beit Hanina.

Palestinian International Campaign to End the Siege on Gaza, 2nd Floor, Alhalabi Building, Shuhada's Street, Gaza City (fax +972-8-288 8727) (end.gaza.siege@gmail.com) (www.end-gaza-siege.ps).

Palestinian-Israeli Peace NGO Forum (Palestinian Office) (CD), c/o Panorama, Al Ahliya St, Ramallah 2045 (+970-2-295 9618) (fax 298 1824) (panorama@panoramacenter.org) (www.peacengo.org). See also under Israel.

Parents' Circle - Families' Forum: Bereaved Palestinian and Israeli Families Supporting Peace and Tolerance (CD CR), 13 Jamal Abed Al-Nasser St, Al-Ram, East Jerusalem (+972-2-234 4551) (fax 234 4553) (alquds@theparentscircle.org) (www.theparentscircle.com). See also under Israel.

Wi'am - Palestinian Conflict Resolution Centre (FR CR), PO Box 1039, Bethlehem, West Bank (+970-2-277 0513) (fax) (zoughbi@alaslah.org) (alaslah.org).

Windows - Israeli-Palestinian Friendship Centre (CD), PO Box 352, Ramallah (office@win-peace.org) (www.win-peace.org). See also in Israel.

Women's International League for Peace and Freedom (Palestine Section) (WL), c/o Hanan Awwad, Wadi-Al-Juz, 4 Al-Khaldi St, East Jerusalem (+972-2-628 8079) (fax 626 4620) (wilpf-palestine@hotmail.com).

PAPUA NEW GUINEA

Centre for Environmental Law and Community Rights [CELCOR] (FE), Suite 1 - Level 1, Malangan House, PO Box 4373, Boroko NCD (+675-323 4509) (fax 311 2106).

PARAGUAY

Amnistía Internacional Paraguay (AI), Dr Hassler 5229 - e/ Cruz del Defensor y Cruz del Chaco, Bsrrio Villa Mora, Asunción (+595-21-604822) (fax 663272) (ai-info@py.amnesty.org) (www.amnesty.org).

Movimiento Objeción de Conciencia - Paraguay [MOC-PY] (WR), Teniente Fariña Nº 386 e/ Caballero e Iturbe, Asunción (moc_py.org).

SERPAJ-Paraguay (HR PA), Calle Teniente Prieto 354 - entre Dr Facundo Insfran y Tte Rodi, Asunción (+595-21-481333) (serpajpy@serpajpy.org.py) (www.serpajpy.org.py).

PERU

Asociación Pro Derechos Humanos [APRODEH] (HR), Jr Pachacútec 980, Jesus Maria, Lima (+51-1-424 7057) (www.aprodeh.org.pe).

Asociación pro-Naciones Unidas del PerÚ (UN), Casilla 1240, Arequipa (+51-54-226039).

PHILIPPINES

Aksyon para sa Kapayapaan at Katarungan (Action for Peace and Justice) - Center for Active Non-Violence [AKKAPKA-CANV] (FR TW HR EL), Rm 222, Administration Bldg, Pius XII Catholic Centre, 1175 UN Avenue, Paco, 1007 Manila (+63-2-526 0103) (fax 400 0823) (akkapka.canv84@gmail.com).

Legal Rights and Natural Resources Center - Kasama sa Kalikasan [LRC-KSK] (FE HR), 24A Malingap St, Teacher's Village, Quezon City 1101 (+63-2-441 0858) (lrcksk@lrcksk.org) (www.lrcksk.org).

Philippine Physicians for the Prevention of Nuclear War (IP), c/o Medical Action Group, 45 Saint Mary St, Cubao, 1100 Quezon City (edelizahernandez@yahoo.com).

Task Force Detainees of the Philippines [TFDP] (HR), 45 Saint Mary St, Cubao, 1109 Quezon City (+63-2-437 8054) (fax 911 3643) (main.tfdp.net).

Women's International League for Peace and Freedom (WL), Rosario T Padilla, 129-A Matahimik Street - UP Village, Diliman, 1101 Quezon City (wilpf_phil@yahoo.com).

POLAND

Greenpeace Poland (GP), Ul Lirowa 13, 02387 Warszawa (+48-22-851 2642) (fax 489 6064) (info@greenpeace.pl) (www.greenpeace.pl).

Pax Christi (PC), Ul Mieroslawskiego 6, 01549 Warszawa (+48-22-840 3766) (fax 817 0344) (ryzenko@poczta.onet.pl).

Servas Polska (SE), c/o Anna Zakrzewska, Ul Kabacki Dukt 16 m 70, 02798 Warszawa (+48-22-321 6493) (aissa@servas.pl) (servas.pl).

PORTUGAL

Amnistia Internacional Portugal (AI), Av Infante Santo 42 - 2º, 1350-179 Lisboa (+351-21 386 1652) (fax 21 386 1782) (aiportugal@amnistia-internacional.pt) (www.amnistia-internacional.pt).

Associação das Nações Unidas Portugal (UN), Rua do Almada 679 - 1º - S 103, 4050-039 Porto (+351-22 200 7767) (fax 22 200 7868) (anuportugal@gmail.com) (www.anup.pt).

Associação dos Médicos Portugueses para a Prevenção da Guerra Nuclear [AMPPGN] (IP), c/o ICBAS, Universidade de Porto, Rua de J Viterbo Ferreira 228, 4050-313 Porto (+351-22 042 8011).

Conselho Português para a Paz e Cooperação [CPPC] (WP ND DA), Rua Rodrigo da Fonseca 56-2º, 1250-193 Lisboa (+351-21 386 3375) (fax 21 386 3221) (conselhopaz@cppc.pt) (www.cppc.pt). Portuguese Council for Peace and Co-operation.

Observatório Género e Violência Armada / Observatory on Gender and Armed Violence [OGIVA] (DA HR), Centro Estudos Sociais, Colégio de S Jerónimo, Apartado 3087, 3000-995 Coimbra (+351-239 855593) (fax 239 855589) (ogiva@ces.uc.pt) (www.ces.uc.pt/ogiva).

Partido Ecologista - Os Verdes (EL), Av D Carlos I - 146 - 1º Dto, 1200-651 Lisboa (+351-21 396 0291) (fax 21 396 0424) (pev@osverdes.pt) (www.osverdes.pt). Green Party.

Tamera Peace Research Centre (EL PO RP), CP 1, 7630-303 Colos (+351-283 635306) (office@tamera.org) (www.tamera.org).

PUERTO RICO

Ecumenical and Inter-Religious Coalition of Puerto Rico (RP), c/o Sociedad Biblica de Puerto Rico, PO Box 21095, San Juan 00928-1095. Affiliated to Religions for Peace International.

RUSSIA

Andrei Sakharov Museum / Peace, Progress and Human Rights Centre (HR), 57 Zemlyaynou Val - Building 6, 105120 Moskva (+7-495-623 4420) (fax 917 2635) (secretary@sakharov-center.u) (www.sakharov-center.ru).

Bellona Russia - St Petersburg (EL), Suvorovskiy Pr 59, 191015 Sankt-Peterburg (+7-812-275 7761) (fax 719 8843) (mail@bellona.ru) (www.bellona.ru). Environment and Rights. Main office in Norway.

Dom Druzeiv v Moskvye / Friends' House Moscow (SF), Sukharevskaya M - pl 6 - str 1, 127051 Moskva (+7-903-664 1075) (dd.moskva@gmail.com) (friendshousemoscow.org).

Dom Mira i Nyenasiliya / House of Peace and Nonviolence (PC), a/ya 33, 191002 Sankt-Peterburg (+7-951-644 8052) (peacehouse.spb@gmail.com) (www.peacehouse.ru).

Federatsiya Mira i Soglasiya / International Federation for Peace and Conciliation [IFPC] (WP), 36 Prospekt Mira, 129090 Moskva (+7-495-680 3576) (fax 688 9587) (vik@ifpc.ru) (www.ifpc.ru). Mir i Soglasiye.

Fond Zashchitiy Glanosti / Glasnost Defence Foundation (HR), 4 Zubovsky Bulevard - Of 438, 119992 Moskva (+7-495-637 4947) (fax 637 4420) (simonov@gdf.ru) (www.gdf.ru).

Greenpeace Russia (GP), Lyeningradskiy prospect - d 26 - k 1, 125040 Moskva (+7-495-988 7460) (fax) (info@greenpeace.ru) (www.greenpeace.org/russia).

Interchurch Partnership - Peace Resarch Centre (PC RE), PO Box 31, 191002 Sankt-Peterburg (+7-812-764 0423) (fax 764 6695) (mshishova@yahoo.com).

Memorial (HR CD), Malyi Karetnyi pereulok 12, 127051 Moskva (+7-495-650 7883) (fax 609 0694) (info@memo.ru) (www.memo.ru).

Moskovskaya Shkola Prav Cheloveka / Moscow School of Human Rights (HR), Luchnikov Per 4 - p3 - k2, 101000 Moskva (+7-495-577 6904) (fax) (mshr@mshr-ngo.ru) (www.mshr.ngo.ru).

Nyemyetsko-Russkiy Obmyen / Deutscher-Russischer Austausch [NRO] (CD), Ligovski Pr 87 - Ofis 300, 191040 Sankt-Peterburg (+7-812-718 3793) (fax 718 3791) (nro@obmen.org) (www.obmen.org). German-Russian Exchange.

Pravo na Zhizn i Grazhdanskoye Dostoynstvo / Right to Life and Human Dignity Society (HR CR RE PC), Luchnikov Per 4 - k19, 103982 Moskva (+7-495-206 8589) (fax 206 8853) (vky@co.ru). Against death penalty and torture.

Russian Physicians for the Prevention of Nuclear War [RPPNW] (IP), Ul Solyanka 14, 109544 Moskva (+7-495-298 2146) (fax 298 2161) (ippnwrus@mail.ru).

RUSSIA

Soldatskiye Matyeri Sankt-Peterburg / Soldiers' Mothers of St Petersburg (HR PA PC), Ul Razyezzhaya 9, 191002 Sankt-Peterburg (+7-812-712 4199) (fax 712 5058) (soldiersmothers@yandex.ru) (www.soldiersmothers.ru).

Tsenter po Isledovaniyu Problem Mira / Centre for Peace Research (RE), Russian Academy of Sciences, Profsoyuznaya Str 23, 117859 Moskva.
Ways to Security.

Tsentr Mezhnatsionalnovo Sotrudnichestva / Centre for Interethnic Co-operation (CR CD), a/ya 8, 127055 Moskva (+7-499-972 6807) (center@interethnic.org) (www.interethnic.org).

RWANDA

Life & Peace Institute - DR Congo (RE RP), PO Box 64, Cyangugu (+243-81-249 4489) (pieter.vanholder@life-peace.org) (www.life-peace.org).

Peace & Conflict Resolution Project (of Bukavu, DR Congo) [PCR] (CR), PO Box 37, Cyangugu (+243-993-463279) (peacecrp@yahoo.com) (www.peaceconflictresolutionproject.webs.com). Operates in Bukavu, eastern Congo.

Shalom - Educating for Peace (RE), PO Box 6210, Kigali (basajd@yahoo.fr).

SERBIA

Autonomni ženski Centar / Autonomous Women's Centre Against Sexual Violence [AZC/AWC] (HR), Tiršova 5a, 11000 Beograd (+381-11-268 7190) (fax) (azc@azc.org.rs) (www.womenngo.org.rs).

Beogradski Forum za Svet Ravnopravnih / Belgrade Forum for a World of Equals [Beoforum] (WP), Sremska Broj 6 - IV sprat, 11000 Beograd (+381-11-328 3778) (beoforum@gmail.com) (www.beoforum.rs).

Centar za Nenasilnu Akciju - Beograd / Centre for Nonviolent Action - Belgrade [CNA] (CR PA RE CD), Čika Ljubina 6, 11000 Beograd (+381-11-263 7603) (fax) (cna.beograd@nenasilje.org) (www.nenasilje.org).
See also in Bosnia-Herzegovina.

Centre for Applied NonViolent Action and Strategies [CANVAS], Gandijeva 76a, 11070 Novi Beograd (+381-11-222 8331) (fax 222 8336) (office@canvasopedia.org) (www.canvasopedia.org).

Serbian Physicians for Peace (IP), c/o Dr Milan Popović, Kantaniceva 10a, 11000 Beograd (+381-11-243 9203).

Žene U Crnom Protiv Rata / Women in Black Against War (WR), Jug Bogdanova 18/V, 11000 Beograd (+381-11-262 3225) (zeneucrnombeograd@gmail.com) (www.zeneucrnom.org).

SIERRA LEONE

Peacelinks Sierra Leone (PO PA CR), Apt 2 - 4th Floor, 17/22 Circular Rd, Freetown (+232-25-213458) (fax 22-224439) (peacelinks2@yahoo.com) (peace-links.org).

Sierra Leone Action Network on Small Arms [SLANSA] (DA AT), c/o YWCA Building, Bismarck-Johnson St, Freetown (slansa2001@yahoo.com).

SINGAPORE

Inter-Religious Organisation - Singapore (RP), Palmer House, 70 Palmer Rd - 05-01/02, Singapore 079427 (+65-6221 9858) (fax 6221 9212) (irosingapore@gmail.com) (iro.sg).
Affiliate of Religions for Peace International.

United Nations Association of Singapore [UNAS] (UN), PO Box 351, Tanglin Post Office, Singapore 912412 (+65-6792 0026) (sctham@unas.org.sg) (www.unas.org.sg).
World Forum.

SLOVAKIA

Priatelia Zeme Slovensko / Friends of the Earth Slovakia (FE), Komenského 21, 97401 Banská Bystrica (+421-48-412 3859) (fax) (foe@priateliazeme.sk) (www.priateliazeme.sk).

SLOVENIA

Društvo za Združene narode za Slovenijo / United Nations Association of Slovenia [DZNS/UNAS] (UN), Cankarjeva 1/II, 1000 Ljubljana (+386-1-251 0708) (fax) (info@unaslovenia.org) (www.unaslovenia.org).

SOMALIA

Centre for Research and Dialogue [CRD] (CR RE), for postal address see under Kenya (+252-1-658666) (fax 5-932355) (crd@crdsomalia.org) (www.crdsomalia.org). Street address: K4 Airport Rd, Mogadishu.

Life & Peace Institute - Somalia and Kenya Programme (RP CR), see under Kenya (michele.cesari@life-peace.org).

Somali Coalition to Ban Landmines [SOCBAL] (DA), Km-4 Street, Hodan District, Mogadishu (+252-1-235730) (somalia_socbal@yahoo.com).

SOUTH AFRICA

Action Support Centre [ASC] (CR), Postnet Suite No 145, Private Bag X9, Melville 2109 (+27-11 482 7442) (fax 11 482 2484) (info@asc.org.za) (www.asc.org.za).

Boycott, Disinvestment and Sanctions Against Israel in South Africa [BDS SA] (HR RA), PO Box 2318, Houghton 2041, Johannesburg (+27-11 403 2097) (fax 86 650 4836) (hadam@bdssouthafrica.com) (www.bdssouthafrica.com).

For explanation of codes and abbreviations, see introduction

Ceasefire Campaign (WR AT), PO Box 31740, Braamfontein, Johannesburg 2017 (+27-11 403 5315) (fax 11 339 7863) (stopwar@csvr.org.za) (www.ceasefire.org.za).

Centre for the Study of Violence and Reconciliation (RE CR HR), PO Box 30778, Braamfontein, Johannesburg 2017 (+27-11 403 5650) (fax 11 339 6785) (info@csvr.org.za) (www.csvr.org.za). Also in Cape Town (+27-21 447 2470).

Desmond Tutu Peace Centre (RE), PO Box 8428, Roggebaai 8012, Cape Town (+27-21 525 1980) (fax 21 525 1990) (info@tutu.org) (www.tutu.org).

Earthlife Africa [ELA] (EL), PO Box 32131, Braamfontein 2107 (+27-11 339 3662) (fax 11 339 3270) (seccp@earthlife.org.za) (www.earthlife.org.za).

GroundWork / Friends of the Earth South Africa (FE), PO Box 2375, Pietermaritzburg 3200 (+27-33 342 5662) (fax 33 342 5665) (team@groundwork.org.za) (www.groundwork.org.za).

GunFree South Africa [GFSA] (AT PA RE), PO Box 12988, Mowbray 7705 (+27-72 544 0573) (fax 86 545 0094) (info@gfsa.org.za) (www.gunfree.org.za).

Institute for Healing of Memories (CR), PO Box 36069, Glosderry 7702 (+27-21 683 6231) (fax 21 683 5747) (info@healingofmemories.co.za) (www.healing-memories.org).

International Centre of Nonviolence [ICON] (RE HR), ML Sultan Campus, Durban University of Technology, PO Box 1334, Durban 4000 (+27-31 373 5499) (icon@dut.ac.za) (www.icon.org.za). Works for a culture of nonviolence.

Quaker Peace Centre (SF CR RE), 3 Rye Rd, Mowbray, Cape Town 7700 (+27-21 685 7800) (fax 21 686 8167) (qpc@qpc.org.za) (www.quaker.org/capetown).

South African Campaign to Ban Landmines [SACBL], c/o Institute for Security Studies, PO Box 1787, Brooklyn Sq, Tshwane (Pretoria) 0075 (+27-12 346 9500) (fax 12 460 0998) (gdube@issafrica.org) (www.issafrica.org).

Trauma Centre for Survivors of Violence and Torture (CR HR), Cowley House, 126 Chapel St, Woodstock, Cape Town 7925 (+27-21 465 7373) (info@trauma.org.za) (www.trauma.org.za).

United Nations Association of South Africa [UNA-SA] (UN), c/o The Coachman's Cottage Museum, PO Box 1256, Somerset West 7129 (+27-21 850 0509) (fax 800 981771) (admin@unasa.org.za) (www.unasa.org.za).

SOUTH SUDAN

Organisation for Nonviolence and Development [ONAD] (WR CR HR), PO Box 508, Juba (+211-921-352592) (onadjuba2011@gmail.com) (www.onadev.org).

SPAIN

Alternativa Antimilitarista - MOC València (WR RA TR), C/ Roger de Flor 8 - baix-dta, 46001 València (+34-96 391 6702) (retirada@pangea.org) (www.insumissia.org).

Alternativa Antimilitarista - Movimiento de Objeción de Conciencia [AA-MOC] (WR RA TR), C/San Cosme y San Damián 24-2º, 28012 Madrid (+34-91 894 5876) (moc.lavapies@nodo50.org) (www.antimilitaristas.org).

Amnistía Internacional España (AI), C/ Fernando VI - 8 - 1º Izda, 28004 Madrid (+34-91 310 1277) (fax 91 319 5334) (info@madrid.es.amnesty.org) (www.es.amnesty.org).

Asociación 11M Afectados del Terrorismo (CR), C/ Puentelarra 7 - locales 3 y 4, 28031 Madrid (+34-91 332 0444) (fax 91 331 9382) (buzon@asociacion11m.org) (www.asociacion11m.org).

Centre Delàs for Peace Studies (Justícia i Pau) (IB RE AT RP), Rivadeneyra 6 - 10è, 08002 Barcelona, Catalunya (+34-93 317 6177) (fax 93 412 5384) (info@centredelas.org) (www.centredelas.org). *Materiales de Trabajo.*

Centro de Investigación para la Paz (RE), Duque de Sesto 40, 28009 Madrid (+34-91 576 3299) (fax 91 577 4726) (cip@fuhem.es) (www.cip-ecosocial.fuhem.es). *Papeles de Relaciones Ecosociales y Cambio Global.*

Ekologistak Martxan Bizkaia (ND EL TW), c/ Pelota 5 - Behea, 48005 Bilbo, Euskadi (+34-94 479 0119) (fax) (bizkaia@ekologistakmartxan.org) (www.ekologistakmartxan.org). *Eco Boletin.*

Escola de Cultura de Pau (RE), Plaça del Coneixement - Edifici MRA (Mòdul Recerca A), UAB, 08193 Bellaterra (+34-93 586 8848) (fax 93 581 3294) (escolapau@uab.cat) (escolapau.uab.cat).

Fundación Cultura de Paz [FCP] (IB WP RE), Calle Velázquez 14 - 3º dcha, 28001 Madrid (+34-91 426 1555) (fax 91 431 6387) (info@fund-culturadepaz.org) (www.fund-culturadepaz.org).

Fundación Seminario de Investigación para la Paz [SIP] (RE), Centro Pignatelli, Pº de la Constitución 6, 50008 Zaragoza (+34-976 217215) (fax 976 230113) (sipp@seipaz.org) (www.seipaz.org).

Gernika Gogoratuz - Peace Research Centre [GGG] (IB RE), Artekale 1-1, 48300 Gernika-Lumo, Bizkaia (+34-94 625 3558) (fax 94 625 6765) (gernikag@gernikagogoratuz.org) (www.gernikagogoratuz.org).

Gesto por la Paz de Euskal Herria - Euskal Herriko Bakearen Aldeko (PA HR RE), Apdo 10152, 48080 Bilbao (+34-94 416 3929) (fax 94 415 3285) (gesto@gesto.org) (www.gesto.org). Association for peace in the Basque Country.

SPAIN

Grup Antimilitarista Tortuga (PA), C/ Ametler 26 - 7ª, 03203 Elx, Alacant (tortuga@nodo50.es) (www.grupotortuga.com). Part of network Alternativa Antimilitarista - MOC.

Instituto de la Paz y los Conflictos (RE), C/ Rector López Argüeta, 18071 Granada (+34-958 244142) (fax 958 248974) (eirene@ugr.es). *Eirene*.

Justicia y Paz - España [CGJP] (RP), Rafael de Riego 16 - 3º dcha, 28045 Madrid (+34-91 506 1828) (juspax@juspax-es.org) (www.juspax-es.org).

Kontzientzi Eragozpen Mugimendua / MOC Euskal Herria [KEM-MOC] (WR AL RA TR), Calle Fica Nº 4 - lonja derecha, 48006 Bilbao, Euskadi (+34-609 469599) (mocbilbao@gmail.com) (www.sinkuartel.org). Part of network Alternativa Antimilitarista - MOC.

Liga Internacional de Mujeres por la Paz y la Libertad (WL), 26-28 bajo - Almería, Zaragoza (wilpf.espanya@gmail.com) (wilpf.es).

MambrÚ - Alternativa Antimilitarista MOC (WR AT SD RA), Centro Social La Pantera Rossa, Calle San Vicente de Paul - 28, 50001 Zaragoza (+34-696 343586) (mambru@nodo50.org) (antimilitaristas.org). Part of network Alternativa Antimilitarista - MOC network.

Moviment per la Pau (PA RE AT), C/ Providència 42, 08024 Barcelona (+34-93 219 3371) (fax 93 213 0890) (movpau@pangea.org). *Lletres de Pau*.

Paz y Cooperación / Peace and Co-operation (IB RE TW), Meléndez Valdés 68 - 4º izq, 28015 Madrid (+34-91 549 6156) (fax 91 543 5282) (pazycooperacion@hotmail.com) (www.peaceandcooperation.org). *Premio Escolar Paz y Cooperación*.

Servas España (SE), Calle de la Roca 5, 08319 Dosrius (servas.spain@gmail.com) (www.servas.es).

Servei Civil Internacional - Catalunya [SCI] (SC PA), c/ Carme 95 - baixos 2a, 08001 Barcelona, Catalunya (+34-93 441 7079) (comunicacio@sci-cat.org) (www.sci-cat.org).

Servicio Civil Internacional [SCI] (SC), c/Ronda de Segovia 55 - oficina 2, 28005 Madrid (+34-91 366 3259) (fax 91 366 2203) (oficina@ongsci.org) (www.ongsci.org).

Survival International (España) [SI] (HR), C/Príncipe 12 - 3º, 28012 Madrid (+34-91 521 7283) (fax 91 523 1420) (info@survival.es) (www.survival.es). *Boletín de Acción Urgente*.

SRI LANKA

Green Movement of Sri Lanka [GMSL] (EL), No 9 First Lane, Wanata Rd, Gangodawila, Nugegoda (+94-11-281 7156) (fax 480 5274) (office@gmsl.lk) (www.gmsl.lk). Consortium of 153 groups and organisations.

Lanka Jathika Sarvodaya Shramadana Sangamaya [Sarvodaya] (HR TW), Damsak Mandira, 98 Rawatawatte Rd, Moratuwa (+94-11-264 7159) (fax 265 6512) (ed@sarvodaya.org) (www.sarvodaya.org).

Mahatma Gandhi Centre (PO PA RE), 22/17 Kalyani Rd, Colombo 00600 (+94-11-250 1825) (fax) (power2people@gandhiswaraj.com) (gandhiswaraj.con).

National Peace Council of Sri Lanka [NPC] (CR RE CD), 12/14 Purana Vihara Rd, Colombo 6 (+94-11-281 8344) (fax 281 9064) (npc@sltnet.lk) (www.peace-srilanka.org). *Paths to Peace*.

SUDAN

Life & Peace Institute (RE RP), PO Box 13119, Khartoum (+249-18-348 0627) (jody.henderson@life-peace.org) (www.life-peace.org).

Peace Desk of New Sudan Council of Churches (RP CD CR HR), see under Kenya.

Sudan Campaign to Ban Landmines [SCBL] (AT), c/o JASMAR Human Security Organisation, Building 127 - Block no 101, Khartoum South, Khartoum (+249-18-348 7524) (fax 349 1701) (aboosamaa@yahoo.com).

Sudan Inter-Religious Council [SIRC] (RP), PO Box 10719, Khartoum (tayibzain@yahoo.com).

Sudanese Organisation for Nonviolence and Development [SONAD] (WR TW HR), PO Box 25, Sudapost Office Eldiyoum Elshargia, Khartoum (+249-155 144977) (fax 155 144988) (sonad.khartoum@gmail.com).

Sudanese Women's Voice for Peace, see under Kenya.

SWEDEN

Folkkampanjen mot Kärnkraft-Kärnvapen / Swedish Anti-Nuclear Movement (EL ND), Pustegränd 1, 11820 Stockholm (+46-8-841490) (info@folkkampanjen.se) (www.folkkampanjen.se). *Medsols*.

Fredens Hus (RE HR), Uppsala Slott - entrance A2, 75237 Uppsala (info@fredenshus.se) (www.fredenshus.se).

Göteborgs Ickevåldsnätverk / Nonviolence Network of Gothenburg (AL PA CR RA), c/o Elisabet Ahlin, Norra Krokslättsgatan 17A, 41264 Göteborg (+46-31-832187) (elisabet.ahlin@gmail.com).

Greenpeace (GP), Rosenlundsgatan 29 B, 11863 Stockholm (+46-8-702 7070) (info.se@greenpeace.org) (www.greenpeace.se).

Internationella Kvinnoförbundet för Fred och Frihet [IKFF] (WL), Norrtullsgatan 45 - 1 tr, 11345 Stockholm (+46-8-702 9810) (info@ikff.se) (www.ikff.se).

Kristna Fredsrörelsen [SweFOR] (FR), Ekumeniska Centret, Box 14038, 16714 Bromma (+46-8-8453 6840) (fax 8453 6829) (info@krf.se) (www.krf.se). *Fredsnytt.*

Kvinnor för Fred / Women for Peace [KFF] (IB ND EL CR), Hammarby Allé 93 - 4tr, 12063 Stockholm (+46-8-667 9727) (kff@telia.com) (www.kvinnorforfred.se).

Life & Peace Institute [LPI] (RP AT RE TW CR), Säbygatan 4, 75323 Uppsala (+46-18-660130) (info@life-peace.org) (www.life-peace.org). *Horn of Africa Bulletin.* Projects in East Africa and Central Africa.

Ofog (WR RA AT ND AL), c/o Göteborgs Fredskommitté, Linnegatan 21, 41304 Göteborg (+46-733-815361) (info@ofog.org) (www.ofog.org).

PBI-Sverige (HR CR), Blomstigen 3, 42437 Angered (+46-31-330 7509) (info@pbi-sweden.org) (www.pbi-sweden.org).

PeaceQuest International (CD CR RE), Box 55913, 10216 Stockholm (+46-8-5592 1180) (info@peacequest.eu) (www.peacequest.eu).

Servas Sverige (SE), c/o Hanna Fagerström, Johanna Wolls Väg 18, 24436 Kävlinge (sweden@servas.se) (www.servas.se).

Svenska FN-Förbundet (UN), Box 15115, 10465 Stockholm (+46-8-462 2540) (fax 641 8876) (info@fn.se) (www.fn.se). *Världshorisont.*

Svenska Fredskommittén / Swedish Peace Committee [SFK] (DA ND), Tegelviksgatan 40, 11641 Stockholm (info@svenskafredskommitten.nu) (www.svenskafredskommitten.nu).

Svenska Läkare Mot Kärnvapen [SLMK] (IP), Norrtullsgatan 45 - 1 tr, 11345 Stockholm (+46-8-4002 0483) (info@slmk.org) (www.slmk.org).

Sveriges Fredsråd / Swedish Peace Council (IB), Tegelviksgatan 40, 11641 Stockholm (info@FredNu.se) (www.frednu.se/sveriges-fredsrad). National federation.

Swedish Peace and Arbitration Society / Svenska Freds- och Skiljedomsföreningen [SPAS] (WR IB AT), Polhemsgatan 4, 11236 Stockholm (+46-8-5580 3180) (info@svenskafreds.se) (www.svenskafreds.se). *Pax.*

Vännernas Samfund (Kväkarna) (SF), Box 9166, 10272 Stockholm (+46-8-668 6816) (fax) (info@kvakare.se).

SWITZERLAND

Action des Chrétiens pour l'Abolition de la Torture / Aktion der Christen für die Abschaffung der Folter [ACAT-Suisse] (HR), CP 5011, 3001 Berne (+41-31 312 2044) (fax 31 312 5811) (info@acat.ch) (www.acat.ch).

Amnesty International (AI), Speichergasse 33, 3011 Bern (+41-31 307 2222) (fax 31 307 2233) (info@amnesty.ch) (www.amnesty.ch). *Amnesty Magazin(e).*

Appel de Genève / Geneva Call for the Adhesion of Non-State Actors to International Humanitarian Law (HR), PO Box 334, 1211 Genève 4 (+41-22 879 1050) (fax 22 879 1051) (info@genevacall.org) (www.genevacall.org).

APRED - Participative Institute for the Progress of Peace (RE PO PA), Route des Siernes Picaz 46, 1659 Flendruz (+41-79 524 3574) (info@demilitarisation.org) (www.apred.org).

ärzte/ärztinnen für Soziale Verantwortung / Médecins pour une Résponsibilité Sociale [PSR/IPPNW] (IP), Bireggstr 36, 6003 Luzern (+41-41 240 6349) (fax) (sekretariat@ippnw.ch) (www.ippnw.ch).

Basel Peace Office (RE ND), Universität Basel, Petersgraben 27, 4051 Basel (info@baselpeaceoffice.org) (www.baselpeaceoffice.org).

Brethren Service (RP), PO Box 2100, 150 route de Ferney, 1211 Genève 2 (+41-22 791 6330) (brethrenservice@worldcom.ch) (www.brethrenvolunteerservice.org).

Centre for Humanitarian Dialogue (CR RE), 114 Rue de Lausanne, 1202 Genève (+41-22 908 1130) (fax 22 908 1140) (info@hdcentre.org) (www.hdcentre.org).

Centre pour l'Action Non-Violente [CENAC] (WR RP IB), 52 rue de Genève, 1004 Lausanne (+41-21 661 2434) (fax 21 661 2436) (info@non-violence.ch) (www.non-violence.ch).

cfd - the feminist peace organisation (PA CR), Postfach 5761, 3001 Berne (+41-31 300 5060) (info@cfd-ch.org) (www.cfd-ch.org). *cfd-Zeitung.*

ContrAtom - Association Antinucléaire Genevoise (EL), CP 65, 1211 Genève 8 (info@contratom.ch) (www.contratom.ch).

Eirene Suisse (RP TW EL CR), 9 Rue du Valais, 1202 Genève (+41-22 321 8556) (fax) (info@eirenesuisse.ch) (www.eirenesuisse.ch).

Gesellschaft für bedrohte Völker / Société pour les Peuples menacés (HR), Schermenweg 154, 3072 Ostermundigen (+41-31 939 0000) (fax 31 939 0019) (info@gfbv.ch) (www.gfbv.ch).

Grüne Partei der Schweiz / Parti écologiste suisse / Partito ecologista svizzero (EL IB), Waisenhausplatz 21, 3011 Bern (+41-31 326 6660) (fax 31 326 6662) (gruene@gruene.ch) (www.gruene.ch). *Greenfo.* Green party. Grüne / Les Verts / I Verdi.

Greenpeace (GP), Badenerstr 171, Postfach 9320, 8036 Zürich (+41-44 447 4141) (fax 44 447 4199) (gp@greenpeace.ch) (www.greenpeace.org/switzerland).

SWITZERLAND

Groupe pour une Suisse sans Armée / Gruppe für eine Schweiz ohne Armee [GSsA/GSoA] (WR DA ND), Case Postale 151, 1211 Genève 8 (+41-22 320 4676) (gssa@gssa.ch) (www.gssa.ch). *Une Suisse sans Armée.*

Institute for Peace and Dialogue [IPD] (CR CD RE), Hegenheimerstr 175, 4055 Basel (fhuseynli@ipdinstitute.ch) (www.idpinstitute.ch).

MIR Suisse / IFOR Schweiz (FR), Brue 4, 2613 Villeret (+41-32 940 7237) (secretariat@ifor-mir.ch) (ifor-mir.ch).

Neuer Israel Fonds Schweiz - NIF Switzerland (HR), Winkelriedplatz 4, 4053 Basel (+41-61 272 1455) (fax 61 361 2972) (info@nif.ch) (www.mif.ch).

Peace Brigades International - Schweiz/Suisse [PBI] (CD HR CR RE), Gutenbergstr 35, 3011 Bern (+41-31 372 4444) (info@peacebrigades.ch) (www.peacebrigades.ch). *Facing Peace.*

Schweizerische Friedensbewegung (WP), Postfach 2113, 4001 Basel (+41-61 681 0363) (fax 61 681 7632) (mail@friedensbewegung.ch) (www.friedensbewegung.ch).

Schweizerische Friedensstiftung [swisspeace] (RE CR), Sonnenbergstr 17, PO Box, 3001 Bern (+41-31 330 1212) (info@swisspeace.ch) (www.swisspeace.ch).

Schweizerischer Friedensrat / Consiglio Svizzera per pa Pace / Conseil Suisse pour la Paix [SFR] (IB AT EL), Gartenhofstr 7, 8004 Zürich (+41-44 242 9321) (info@friedensrat.ch) (www.friedensrat.ch). *FriZ. Swiss Peace Council.*

Service Civil International - Schweizer Zweig / Branche suisse / Sede svizzera [SCI] (SC), Monbijoustr 32, Postfach 7855, 3001 Bern (+41-31 381 4620) (info@scich.org) (www.scich.org). *Service Civil International.*

Société Religieuse des Amis, Assemblée de Suisse (Quaker) [SYM] (SF), c/o Maison Quaker, 13 Av du Mervelet, 1209 Genève (+41-22 748 4800) (fax 22 748 4819) (symclerk@swiss-quakers.ch) (www.swiss-quakers.ch). *Entre Amis.*

Société Suisse - Nations Unies / Schweizerisches Versicherungsverband (UN), Postfach 762, 6431 Schwyz (info@schweiz-uno.ch) (www.schweiz-uno.ch).

umverkehR (EL), Kalkbreitestrasse 2, Postfach 8214, 8036 Zürich (+41-44 242 7276) (info@umverkehr.ch) (www.umverkehr.ch). Working especially to cut car use.

Weltföderalisten der Schweiz / Fédéralistes mondiaux de Suisse (WF), c/o Hexagon, Graben 5, 6301 Zug (info@weltfoederalisten.ch) (www.weltfoederalisten.ch). Member of World Federalist Movement (WFM).

Women's Internationl League for Peace and Freedom (WL), Postfach 923, 3000 Bern 9 (wilpfschweiz.ch).

SYRIA
Syrian Human Rights Committee [SHRC] (HR), see under Britain. Syrian human rights group in exile in Britain.

TAIWAN
Amnesty International (AI), 3F- No 14 - Lane 165 - Sec 1, Sin-sheng S Rd, Taipei City 106 (+886-2-2709 4162) (fax 2709 4482) (secretariat@amnesty.tw) (www.amnesty.tw).

Chinese Association for Human Rights [CAHR] (HR), 4F-3 - No 23 - Sec 1 - Hangchow S Rd, Taipei 10053 (+886-2-3393 6900) (fax 2395 7399) (humanright@cahr.org.tw) (www.cahr.org.tw).

Greenpeace East Asia - Taipei Office (GP), No 10, Lane 83, Section 1, Roosevelt Rd, Zhongzheng District, Taipei City 10093 (+886-2-2321 5006) (fax 2321 3209) (inquiry.tw@greenpeace.org) (www.greenpeace.org/eastasia).

John Paul II Peace Institute / Fujen Peace Centre (RP), Fujen Catholic University, 24205 Hsinchuang, Taipei County (+886-2-2905 3111) (fax 2905 2170) (peace@mail.fju.edu.tw) (peace.fjac.fju.edu.tw). *Peace Papers.*

TANZANIA
United Nations Association of Tanzania (UN), PO Box 9182, Dar es Salaam (+255-22-219 9200) (fax 266 8749) (info@una.or.tz) (una.or.tz).

THAILAND
Asian Institute for Human Rights [AIHR] (HR), 109 Soi Sithicon, Suthisarnwinichai Road, Samsennok, Huaykwang, Bangkok 10310 (+66-2 277 6882) (fax) (kalpalatad@aihr.info) (aihr.info).

Greenway Thailand (WC), 40/1 Moo 4 Ban Vihan, Kaow Tambon Vihan, Kaow, Tha Chang district, Singburi 16140 (+66-36 521619) (info@greenwaythailand.org) (www.greenwaythailand.org).

Peace for Burma Coalition [PFB] (HR), c/o Union for Civil Liberty, 109 Suthisamwinichai Rd, Samsennok, Huaykwang, Bangkok 10320 (+66-2 277 3627) (fax 2 276 2183) (peace4burma@gmail.com) (www.peace4burma.blogspot.com). Coalition of Thai and Burmese civil society groups.

TIBET
Tibetan Centre for Human Rights and Democracy (FR HR), see under India. Works for human rights of Tibetans in Tibet.

For explanation of codes and abbreviations, see introduction

TOGO

Amis de la Terre - Togo [ADT] (FE), BP
20190, Lomé (+228-2222 1731)
(fax 2222 1732) (adt-togo@amiterre.tg)
(www.amiterre.tg)

Amnesty International Togo (AI), 2 BP 20013,
Lomé 2 (+228-2222 5820) (fax)
(contact@amnesty.tg) (www.amnesty.tg).
Echos d'AI; Miafé Dzena.

TRINIDAD AND TOBAGO

**United Nations Association of Trinidad &
Tobago [UNATT]** (UN), 106 Woodford Street,
Newtown, Port of Spain (+1 868-623 7645)
(info@unassociationtt.org) (unassociationtt.org)

TUNISIA

**Coalition Nationale Tunisienne contre la Peine
de Mort** (HR), 56 Avenue de la Liberté, 1002
Tunis (+216-2168 7533)
(abolitionpm@gmail.com).
National Coalition Against the Death Penalty.

TURKEY

Barış Derneği / Peace Association of Turkey
(WP), Karanfil Sokak 34/16, Kızılay, Ankara
(+90-312-418 8499) (baris@barisdernegi.org)
(www.barisdernegi.org).

Birleşmiş Milletler Türk Derneği (UN), Atatürk
Bulvarı 223/7, 06680 Kavaklıdere, Ankara
(+90-312-427 2216) (fax 427 4283)
(info@unaturkey.org) (www.unaturkey.org).

Greenpeace Mediterranean (GP), İstiklal
Caddesi Kallavi Sok - No 1 Kat 2, Beyoğlu,
İstanbul (+90-212-292 7619) (fax 292 7622)
(bilgi.tr@greenpeace.org)
(www.greenpeace.org/turkey). See also
Israel, Lebanon.

**İnsan Hakları Derneği / Human Rights
Association [İHD]** (HR), Necatibey Cad 82/11-
12, Kızılay, çankaya, 06430 Ankara
(+90-312-230 3567) (fax 230 1707)
(posta@ihd.org.tr) (www.ihd.org.tr).

**Nükleer Tehlikkeye Karşı Baris ve Çevre Için
Sağlıkçılar Derneği [NÜSED]** (IP), c/o
Mehmet Altinok, Sağlik-2 Sok 6 3/8, Kolej -
Ankara (dboztok@superonline.com).

Peace and Conflict Studies Programme (RE),
Graduate School of Social Sciences,
Hacettepe University, 06800 Beytepe, Ankara
(+90-312-297 8111) (fax 297 6710)
(peace@hacettepe.edu.tr)
(www.peace.hacettepe.edu.tr).

**Şiddetsizlik Egitim ve Arastırma Derneği /
Nonviolent Education and Research
Association** (RE WR), Kuloğlu Mah Güllabici
sok no 16 - Daire 3 (2nd floor), 34433
Cihangir, İstanbul (+90-212-244 1269)
(office@nvrc-sarm.org) (www.nvrc-sarm.org).

**Türkiye İnsan Hakları Vakfı / Human Rights
Foundation of Turkey [TIHV/HRFT]** (HR),
Mithatpaşa Cad - No 49/11 - 6 Kat, 06420
Kızılay / Ankara (+90-312-310 6636) (fax 310
6463) (tihv@tihv.org.tr) (www.tihv.org.tr). In
İstanbul: +90-212-249 3092.

**Türkiye Çevre Vafkı / Environment Foundation
of Turkey [TÇV]** (EL), Tunalı Hilmi Cd 50/20,
Kavaklıdere, 06660 Ankara
(+90-312-425 5508) (fax 418 5118)
(cevre@cevre.org.tr) (www.cevre.org.tr).
Çevre.

Uluslararası Af örgütü Türkiye Şubesi (AI),
Abdülhakhamid Cd 30/5, Talimhane-Taksim,
Beyoğlu/İstanbul (+90-212-361 6217)
(fax 361 6219) (posta@amnesty.org.tr)
(www.amnesty.org.tr).

**Vicdani Ret Derneği / Conscientious Objector
Association [VR-DER]** (WR HR), Osamanğa
Mah Söğutluçeşme Cad - Sevil Pasajı No 74
- Kat 5 - Ofis 108, Kadıköy, İstanbul
(+90-216-345 0100) (fax)
(dernek@vicdaniret.org).
For legalising conscientious objection.

UGANDA

**Justice & Peace Commission of Gulu
Archdiocese** (PC HR), PO Box 200, Gulu
(+256-471-32026) (fax 432860)
(jpcgulu@infocom.co.ug).

Uganda Peace Foundation Initiative [UPFI],
PO Box 123, Kitgum
(www.ugandapeacefoundation.org).

UKRAINE

Mama-86 (EL), Bul Chapaeva 14 - Of 1, 01030
Kiyiv (+380-44-234 6929) (fax)
(info@mama-86.org.ua)
(www.mama-86.org.ua).
Includes anti-nuclear campaigning.

Zeleniy Svit / Green World (FE PA),
Kontaktova Plosha 4, 04070 Kiyiv
(+380-44-417 0283)
(zelenysvit@ukrpack.net)
(www.zelenysvit.org.ua).

UNITED STATES OF AMERICA

**Action Reconciliation Service for Peace - US
[ARSP]** (CD RE), 1501 Cherry St,
Philadelphia, PA 19102 (+1-215-241 7249)
(fax 241 7252) (info@actionreconciliation.org)
(actionreconciliation.org).

AJ Muste Memorial Institute (IB RE WR), 168
Canal St - 6th Flr, New York, NY 10013
(+1-212-533 4335) (info@ajmuste.org)
(www.ajmuste.org).
Muste Notes.

**Al-Awda - The Palestine Right to Return
Coalition** (HR), PO Box 8812, Coral Springs,
FL 33075 (+1-760-918 9441) (fax 918 9442)
(info@al-awda.org) (al-awda.org).

Albert Einstein Institution (RE SD), PO Box
455, East Boston, MA 02128
(+1-617-247 4882) (fax 247 4035)
(einstein@igc.org) (www.aeinstein.org).

Alliance for Global Justice (HR RA EL), 225 E
26th St - Suite 1, Tucson, AZ 85713
(+1-202-540 8336) (afgj@afgj.org) (afgj.org).
Focus on changing US policy towards Latin
America.

USA

Alliance for Humane Biotehcnology (EL HR), 155 21st Ave, San Francisco, CA 94121 (info@humanebiotech.org) (www.humanebiotech.com).

Alliance for Middle East Peace [ALLMEP] (CD), 2550 M St NW, Washington, DC 20037 (+1-202-618 4600) (fax 888-784 4530) (info@allmep.org) (www.allmep.org). Promoting people-to-people coexistence.

Alliance for Nuclear Accountability [ANA] (ND DA EL), 322 4th St NE, Washington, DC 20002 (+1-202-544 0217) (sgordon@ananuclear.org) (www.ananuclear.org).

Alternatives to Violence Project - USA [AVP/USA] (CR PO), 1050 Selby Ave, St Paul, MN 55104 (+1-888-278 7820) (info@avpusa.org) (avpusa.org).

American Civil Liberties Union [ACLU] (HR), 125 Broad St - 18th Floor, New York, NY 10004 (aclu@aclu.org) (www.aclu.org).

American Friends of Neve Shalom / Wahat al-Salam (CD HR PA RE), 229 N Central Ave - Suite 401, Glendale, CA 91203-3541 (+1-818-662 8883) (afnswas@oasisofpeace.org) (www.oasisofpeace.org). Support mixed (Jewish-Palestinian) Israeli village.

American Friends Service Committee [AFSC] (SF RE CR), 1501 Cherry St, Philadelphia, PA 19102 (+1-215-241 7000) (fax 241 7275) (afscinfo@afsc.org) (www.afsc.org). *Quaker Action.*

American Jews for a Just Peace [AJJP] (RA), PO Box 1032, Arlington, MA 02474 (www.ajjp.org).

Americans for Democracy and Human Rights in Bahrain (HR), 1001 Connecticut Ave NW - Suite 205, Washington, DC 20036 (+1-202-621 6141) (adhrb.org).

Amnesty International USA [AIUSA] (AI), 5 Penn Plaza - 16th floor, New York, NY 10001 (+1-212-807 8400) (admin-us@aiusa.org) (www.amnestyusa.org).

Anglican Pacifist Fellowship - US [APF] (RP), c/o Nathaniel W Pierce, 3864 Rumsey Dr, Trappe, MD 21673-1722 (+1-410-476 4556) (nwpierce@verizon.net).

Association of Christians for the Abolition of Torture [ACAT] (HR), PO Box 314, Pleasant Hill, TN 38578-0314 (revhdsmith@starpower.net).

Baptist Peace Fellowship of North America - Bautistas por la Paz [BPFNA] (RP), 300 Hawthorne Lane - Ste 205, Charlotte, NC 28204 (+1-704-521 6051) (fax 521 6053) (bpfna@bpfna.org) (www.bpfna.org). *Baptist Peacemaker.*

Beyond Nuclear (EL ND), 6930 Carroll Ave - Suite 400, Takoma Park, MD 20912 (+1-301-270 2209) (fax 270 4000) (info@beyondnuclear.org) (www.beyondnuclear.org).

Brady Campaign to Prevent Gun Violence (RE HR DA PO), 840 First St NE - Suite 400, Washington, DC 20002 (+1-202-370 8100) (policy@bradymail.org) (www.bradycampaign.org).

Brethren Volunteer Service (PA CD RP), Church of the Brethren, 1451 Dundee Ave, Elgin, IL 60120 (+1-847-742 5100) (fax 429 4394) (bvs@brethren.org) (www.brethrenvolunteerservice.org).

Bruderhof Communities (RP), 101 Woodcrest Dr, Rifton, NY 12471 (+1-845-658 7700) (info@bruderhof.com) (www.bruderhof.com). Also known as Church Communities International.

Buddhist Peace Fellowship [BPF] (FR IB), PO Box 3470, Berkeley, CA 94703 (+1-510-239 3764) (membership@bpf.org) (www.bpf.org). *Turning Wheel Media.*

Campaign for Peace & Democracy [CPD] (IB HR RE), 2808 Broadway - No 12, New York, NY 10025 (+1-212-666 5924) (cpd@igc.org) (www.cpdweb.org).

Cat Lovers Against the Bomb [CLAB] (ND AT HR), c/o Nebraskans for peace, PO Box 83466, Lincoln, NE 68501-3466 (+1-402-475 4620) (fax 483 4108) (catcal@aol.com) (www.catloversagainstthebomb.org). *Calendar.*

Catholic Peace Fellowship (RP PA), PO Box 4232, South Bend, IN 46634 (+1-574-232 2811) (staff@catholicpeacefellowship.org) (www.catholicpeacefellowship.org). Promotes conscientious objection.

Catholic Worker Movement (AL RP PA), 36 E 1st St, New York, NY 10003 (+1-212-777 9617). *The Catholic Worker.*

Center for Applied Conflict Management [CACM] (RE CR), Kent State University, PO Box 5190, Kent, OH 44242-0001 (+1-330-672 3143) (fax 672 3362) (cacm@kent.edu) (www.kent.edu/cacm).

Center for Citizen Initiatives [CCI] (CD), 820 N Delaware St - Ste 405, San Mateo, CA 94401 (+1-650-458 8115) (info@ccisf.org) (ccisf.org). Organise US-Russia citizen exchanges.

Center for Civilians in Conflict, 1210 18th St NW - 4th Floor, Washington, DC 20036 (+1-202-558 6958) (fax 623-321 7076) (info@civiliansinconflict.org) (civiliansinconflict.org).

Center for Genetics and Society [CGS] (EL HR), 1936 University Ave - Suite 350, Berrkeley, CA 94794 (+1-510-625 0819) (fax 665 8760) (info@geneticsandsociety.org) (www.geneticsandsociety.org).

Center for Jewish Nonviolence [CJNV] (PA DA HR), c/o T'ruah - The Rabbinic Call for Human Rights, 266 West 37th St - Suite 803,

New York, NY 10018 (CJNV.campaigns@gmail.com) (centerforjewishnonviolence.org). Organises visits to Israel for nonviolent action.

Center for Nonviolence and Peace Studies [CNPS] (RE CR PO), University of Rhode Island, 74 Lower College Rd - MCC 202, Kingston, RI 02881 (+1-401-874 2875) (fax 874 9108) (nonviolence@etal.uri.edu) (www.uri.edu/nonviolence). *Become the Change.*

Center for Nonviolent Solutions (RE CR), 901 Pleasant St, Worcester, MA 01602 (+1-774-641 1566) (inquiry@nonviolentsolution.org) (www.nonviolentsolution.org).

Center for Restorative Justice & Peacemaking (CR RE), University of Minnesota, 105 Peters Hall, 1404 Gortner Ave, Saint Paul, MN 55108 (+1-612-625 1220) (fax 624 3744) (www.cehd.umn.edu/ssw/rjp). For community-based response to crime and violence.

Center for the Study and Promotion of Zones of Peace (RE), 139 Kuulei Rd, Kailua, HI 96734 (+1-808-263 4015) (fax) (lop-rey.zop-hi@worldnet.att.net).

Center for Victims of Torture (HR RE), 2356 University Ave W - Suite 430, Saint Paul, MN 55114 (+1-612-436 4800) (cvt@cvt.org) (www.cvt.org).

Center on Conscience & War [CCW] (PA HR), 1830 Connecticut Ave NW, Washington, DC 20009-5706 (+1-202-483 2220) (fax 483 1246) (ccw@CenteronConscience.org) (www.centeronconscience.org). *The Reporter for Conscience' sake.*

Christian Peacemaker Teams [CPT] (RP PA RA), PO Box 6508, Chicago, IL 60680-6508 (+1-773-376 0550) (fax 376 0549) (peacemakers@cpt.org) (www.cpt.org).

Co-operation Ireland (USA) (CD), 1501 Broadway - Suite 2600 (Attn Richard Pino), NY 10036 (www.cooperationireland.org).

Coalition Against Nukes [CAN] (EL ND), c/o NIRS, 6930 Carroll Ave - No 340, Takoma Park, MD 20912 (coalitionagainstnukes.org). Established after March 2011 Fukushima meltdowns.

Coalition to Stop Gun Violence (DA AT), 1424 L Street NW - Suite 2-1, Washington, DC 20005 (+1-202-408 0061) (csgv@csgv.org) (www.csgv.org).

CODEPINK: Women for Peace (PA), 2010 Linden Ave, Venice, CA 90291 (+1-310-827 4320) (fax 827 4547) (info@codepink.org) (www.codepink.org). A women-initiated grassroots peace campaign.

Colgate University Peace & Conflict Studies Program (RE CR), 13 Oak Dr, Hamilton, NY 13346-1398 (+1-315-228 7806) (fax 228 7121) (peace@colgate.edu) (www.colgate.edu/departments/ peacestudies/).

Committee Opposed to Militarism & the Draft [COMD] (PA), PO Box 15195, San Diego, CA 92175 (+1-760-753 7518) (comd@comdsd.org) (www.comdsd.org). *Draft NOtices.*

Common Defense Campaign [CDC] (RE), c/o William Goodfellow, Centre for International Policy, 2000 M St NW - Suite 720, Washington, DC 20036-3327 (+1-202-232 3317) (wcg@ciponline.org) (www.ciponline.org). Previously the Project on Defense Alternatives.

Community of Christ Peace and Justice Ministries (RP CR TW HR), 1001 W Walnut, Independence, MO 64050-3562 (+1-816-833 1000) (fax 521 3082) (shalom@CofChrist.org) (www.CofChrist.org/peacejustice). *Herald.*

Council for Responsible Genetics [CRG] (EL HR), 5 Upland Rd - Suite 3, Cambridge, MA 02140 (+1-617-868 0870) (fax 491 5344) (crg@gene-watch.org) (www.councilforresponsiblegenetics.org). *GeneWatch.*

Courage to Resist (WR HR), 484 Lake Park Ave - No 41, Oakland, CA 94610 (+1-510-488 3559) (www.couragetoresist.org). Supports public military refusers facing court.

Creative Response to Conflict [CRC] (FR CR PO), PO Box 271, Nyack, NY 10960-0271 (+1-845-353 1796) (fax 358 4924) (inquiries@crc-global.org) (crc-global.org).

Creativity for Peace (CD), 369 Montezuma Ave - No 566, Santa Fe, NM 87501 (+1-505-982 3765) (dottie@creativityforpeace.com) (www.creativityforpeace.com).

Cultural Survival [CS] (HR), 2067 Massachusetts Ave, Cambridge, MA 02140 (+1-617-441 5400) (fax 441 5417) (culturalsurvival@cs.org) (www.cs.org).

Cumberland Center for Justice and Peace [CCJP] (CR HR RE EL), PO Box 307, Sewanee, TN 37375 (+1-931-636 7527) (contact@ccjp.org) (www.ccjp.org). *Local Action and Beyond.*

Death Penalty Information Center (HR RE), 1015 18th St NW - Suite 704, Washington, DC 20036 (+1-202-289 2275) (dpic@deathpenaltyinfo.org) (www.deathpenaltyinfo.org).

Democratic World Federalists (WF), 55 New Montgomery St - Suite 55, San Francisco, CA 94105 (+1-415-227 4880) (dwfed@dwfed.org) (www.dwfed.org).

East Timor and Indonesia Action Network [ETAN] (HR TW), PO Box 21873, Brooklyn, New York, NY 11202-1873 (+1-718-596 7668) (etan@etan.org) (www.etan.org).

Ecumenical Accompaniment Programme in Palestine and Israel - USA [EAPPI-USA] (RP HR), c/o Steve Weaver, Church World Service, 475 Riverside Dr - Suite 700, New York, NY 10115 (info@eappi-us.org) (www.eappi-us.org).

Environmentalists Against War (EL DA ND PA AT), PO Box 27, Berkeley, CA 94701 (+1-510-843 3343) (info@envirosagainstwar.org) (www.envirosagainstwar.org).

Episcopal Peace Fellowship [EPF] (FR CD), PO Box 15, Claysburg, PA 16625 (+1-312-922 8628) (epf@epfnational.org) (www.epfnational.org).

Equal Justice USA (HR), 20 Jay St - Suite 808, Brooklyn, NYC, NY 11201 (+1-718-801 8940) (fax 801 8947) (info@ejusa.org) (www.ejusa.org). Against executions.

Everytown for Gun Safety (DA), PO Box 4184, New York, NY 10163 (+1-646-324 8250) (everytown.org). Working to end gun violence.

Farms Not Arms - Peace Roots Alliance [PRA] (DA EL), 425 Farm Rd - Suite 5, Summertown, TN 38483 (+1-931-964 2119) (fna_info@farmsnotarms.org) (www.farmsnotarms.org). Also West Coast office (+1-707-765 0196).

Fellowship for Intentional Community [FIC] (PO CR AL), 23 Dancing Rabbit Lane, Rutledge, MO 63563 (+1-660-883 5545) (fic@ic.org) (www.ic.org). *Communities.*

Fellowship of Reconciliation [FOR] (FR WR), 521 N Broaday, Nyack, NY 10960-0271 (+1-845-358 4601) (fax 358 4924) (communications@forusa.org) (www.forusa.org). *Fellowship.*

Food Not Bombs [FnB-US] (PA PO RA), PO Box 424, Arroyo Seco, NM 87514 (+1-575-770 3377) (menu@foodnotbombs.net) (www.foodnotbombs.net).

Footprints for Peace (ND EL), 1225 North Bend Rd, Cincinnati, OH 45224 (jim@footprintsforpeace.org) (www.footprintsforpeace.org).

Franciscan Action Network (RP EL HR), PO Box 29106, Washington, DC 20017 (+1-202-527 7575) (fax 527 7576) (info@franciscanaction.org) (franciscanaction.org).

Friends for a Nonviolent World (PA PO CR), 1050 Selby Ave, Saint Paul, MN 55104 (+1-651-917 0383) (info@fnvw.org) (www.fnvw.org).

Friends of Peace Pilgrim (PO CR), PO Box 2207, Shelton, CT 06484-1841 (+1-203-926 1581) (friends@peacepilgrim.org) (www.peacepilgrim.org).

Friends of the Earth (FE), 1100 15th St NW - 11th Floor, Washington, DC 20005 (+1-202-783 7400) (fax 783 0444) (foe@foe.org) (www.foe.org).

Friends Peace Teams [FPT] (SF CR), 1001 Park Ave, St Louis, MO 63104 (+1-314-588 1122) (Office@FriendsPeaceTeams.org) (friendspeaceteams.org). *PeaceWays.*

Genocide Watch (HR RE), 3351 N Fairfax Dr - MS4D3, Arlington, VA 22201 (+1-202-643 1405) (fax 703-993 1302) (communications@genocidewatch.org) (www.genocidewatch.com).

Global Exchange (HR RE CD TW), 2017 Mission St - 2nd floor, San Francisco, CA 94110 (+1-415-255 7296) (fax 255 7498) (www.globalexchange.org). *Global Exchange.*

Global Green USA (EL AT CR), 1617 Broadway - 2nd floor, Santa Monica, CA 90404 (+1-310-581 2700) (fax 581 2702) (social@globalgreen.org) (www.globalgreen.org).

Global Majority (CR RE), 411 Pacific St - Suite 318, Monterey, CA 93940 (+1-831-372 5518) (fax 372 5519) (info@globalmajority.net) (globalmajority.org). Promoting peace through dialogue.

Global Meditations Network (CR PO), c/o Barbara Wolf, 218 Dartmouth St, Rochester, NY 14607 (bjwolf@globalmeditations.com) (www.globalmeditations.com).

Global Security Institute [GSI] (ND RE WF), 866 United Natioins Plaza - Suite 4050, New York, NY 10017 (+1-646-289 5170) (fax 289 5171) (general@gsinstitute.org) (www.gsinstitute.org).

Global Witness (EL HR TW CR), 1100 17th St NW - Suite 501, Washington, DC 20036 (+1-202-827 8673) (www.globalwitness.org). Also in Britain.

GMO Free USA (EL), PO Box 458, Unionville, CT 06085 (info@gmofreeusa.org) (www.gmofreeusa.org).

Green Party of the United States (EL HR CD), PO Box 75075, Washington, DC 20013 (+1-202-319 7191) (info@gp.org) (www.gp.org).

Greenpeace USA (GP), 702 H St NW - Suite 300, Washington, DC 20001 (+1-202-462 1177) (fax 462 4507) (info@wdc.greenpeace.org) (www.greenpeace.org/usa). *Greenpeace.*

Ground Zero Center for Nonviolent Action (ND PA RA), 16159 Clear Creek Rd NW, Poulsbo, WA 98370 (+1-360-930 8697) (info@gzcenter.org) (gzcenter.org). *Ground Zero.*

Guatemala Human Rights Commission USA [GHRC] (HR), 3321 12th St NE, Washington, DC 20017 (+1-202-529 6599) (fax 526 4611) (ghrc-usa@ghrc-usa.org) (www.ghrc-usa.org). *El Quetzal.*

Hand in Hand (PO CD RE), PO Box 80102, Portland, OR 97280 (+1-503-892 2962) (info@handinhandk12.org) (www.handinhandk12.org). Supports integrated education in Israel.

If Americans Knew, 9208 NE Highway 99 - Suite 107-207, Vancouver, WA 98665 (+1-202-631 4060) (fax 815-301 8048) (contact@IfAmericansKnew.org) (www.ifamericansknew.org).

Institute for Food and Development Policy /
Food First (RE TW EL), 398 60th St,
Oakland, CA 94618 (+1-510-654 4400)
(fax 654 4551) (info@foodfirst.org)
(www.foodfirst.org)

Institute for Inclusive Security (RE CR), 1615
M St NW - Suite 850, Washington, DC 20036
(+1-202-403 2000) (fax 808 7070)
(info@inclusivesecurity.org)
(www.inclusivesecurity.org). Promotes
women's contributions to peacebuilding.

Institute for Middle East Understanding [IMEU]
(RE CD), 2913 El Camino Real - No 436,
Tustin, CA 92782 (+1-718-514 9662)
(info@imeu.org) (imeu.org). Provides
research and experts about Palestine.

Institute for Social Ecology (EL AL PO), PO
Box 48, Plainfield, VT 05667
(info@social-ecology.org)
(www.social-ecology.org).

Institute for the Study & Practice of
Nonviolence (RE CR RP), 265 Oxford St,
Providence, RI 02905 (+1-401-785 2320)
(fax 270 5490)
(catherine@nonviolenceinstitute.org)
(www.nonviolenceinstitute.org).

Interfaith Peace-Builders (RP CD CR), 1628
16th St NW, Washington, DC 20009
(+1-202-244 0821) (fax -866-936 1650)
(office@ifpb.org) (www.ifpb.org).
Send delegations to Israel/Palestine.

International Center on Nonviolent Conflict
[ICNC] (RE SD), PO Box 27606, Washington,
DC 20038 (+1-202-416 4720) (fax 466 5918)
(icnc@nonviolent-conflict.org)
(www.nonviolent-conflict.org).

International Rivers (FE HR), 2150 Allston
Way - Suite 300, Berkeley, CA 94704-1378
(+1-510-848 1155) (fax 848 1008)
(info@internationalrivers.org)
(www.internationalrivers.org).
World Rivers Review.

Israeli-Palestinian Confederation Committee
(CD CR), 15915 Ventura Blvd - No 302,
Encino, CA 91436 (+1-818-317 7110)
(mail@aboutipc.org) (www.aboutipc.org).

Jewish Peace Fellowship [JPF] (FR), Box 271,
Nyack, NY 10960-0271 (+1-845-358 4601)
(fax 358 4924) (jpf@forusa.org)
(www.jewishpeacefellowship.org). *Shalom.*

Jewish Voice for Peace [JVP] (HR CR RA),
1611 Telegraph Ave - Suite 1020, Oakland,
CA 94612 (+1-510-465 1777) (fax 465 1616)
(info@jvp.org) (jewishvoiceforpeace.org).
Promotes US policy based on human rights.

Just Peace Circles (RE CD CR), 5085 Green
Bridge Rd, Dayton, MD 21036 (+1-202-329
4667) (info@justpeacecircles.org)
(justpeacecircles.org).

Kansas Institute for Peace and Conflict
Resolution [KIPCOR] (RE CR), Bethel
College, 300 E 27th St, North Newton, KS
67117 (+1-316-284 5217) (fax 284 5379)
(kipcor@bethelks.edu) (www.kipcor.org).
Formerly Kansas Peace Institute.

Karuna Center for Peacebuilding [KCP] (CR
HR RE), 447 West St, Amherst, MA 01002
(+1-413-256 3800) (fax 256 3802)
(info@karunacenter.org)
(www.karunacenter.org).

Lawyers' Committee on Nuclear Policy [LCNP]
(ND AT DA), 866 UN Plaza - Suite 4050,
New York, NY 10017-1830 (+1-212-818
1861) (fax 818 1857) (contact@lcnp.org)
(www.lcnp.org).

Mahatma Gandhi Center for Global
Nonviolence (RE), James Madison
University, MSC 2604, The Annex, 725 S
Mason St, Harrisonburg, VA 22807
(+1-540-568 4060) (fax 568 7251)
(GandhiCenter@jmu.edu)
(www.jmu.edu/gandhicenter).

Mahatma Gandhi Library (RE), c/o Atul
Kothari, 4526 Bermuda Dr, Sugar Land, TX
77479 (+1-281-531 1977) (fax 713-785 6252)
(info@gandhilibrary.org)
(www.gandhilibrary.org).

Martin Luther King Jr Center for Nonviolent
Social Change (HR RE PO), 449 Auburn Av
NE, Atlanta, GA 30312 (+1-404-526 8900)
(www.thekingcenter.org).

Martin Luther King Jr Research and Education
Institute (RE CR), Cypress Hall D, Stanford
University, Stanford, CA 94305-4146
(+1-650-723 2092) (fax 723 2093)
(kinginstitute.info).

Maryknoll Office for Global Concerns (PC EL
RE), 200 New York Ave NW, Washington,
DC 20001 (+1-202-832 1780) (fax 832 5195)
(ogc@maryknoll.org) (www.maryknoll.org).

Matsunaga Institute for Peace and Conflict
Resolution (RE CR), University of Hawaii,
2424 Maile Way - Saunders 723, Honolulu,
HI 96822 (+1-808-956 4237) (fax 956 0950)
(uhip@hawaii.edu) (peaceinstitute.hawaii.edu).

Minnesota Alliance of Peacemakers (FR UN
WL PC), PO Box 19573, Minneapolis, MN
55419 (info@mapm.org) (www.mapm.org).
Umbrella group of many local organisations.

MK Gandhi Institute for Nonviolence (RE), 929
S Plymouth Ave, Rochester, NY 14608
(+1-585-463 3266) (fax 276 0203)
(kmiller@admin.rochester.edu)
(www.gandhiinstitute.org).

Murder Victims' Families for Human Rights
(HR CR RE PO), 2161 Massachusetts Ave,
Cambridge, MA 02140 (+1-617-491 9600)
(info@murdervictimsfamilies.org)
(www.mvfhr.org). Oppose death penalty.

Musicians and Fine Artists for World Peace
[MFAWP] (PO CD), 3274 Andrea St - Apt C,
Las Vegas, NV 89102 (+1-415-424 7238)
(bflyspirit8@aol.com)
(www.reverbnation.com/musiciansforpeace).

National Campaign for a Peace Tax Fund
[NCPTF] (TR), 2121 Decatur Pl NW,
Washington, DC 20008 (+1-202-483 3751)
(info@peacetaxfund.org)
(www.peacetaxfund.org).
Peace Tax Fund Update.

USA

National Coalition to Abolish the Death Penalty [NCADP] (HR), 1620 L St NW - Suite 250, Washington, DC 20036 (+1-202-331 4090) (info@ncadp.org) (www.ncadp.org).

National Network Opposing the Militarization of Youth [NNOMY] (DA PO), c/o AFSC Wage Peace Program, 65 Ninth St, San Francisco, CA 94103 (+1-760-634 3604) (admin@nnomy.org) (www.nnomy.org).

National Peace Academy [NPA] (RE), PO Box 2024, San Mateo, CA 94401 (+1-650-918 6901) (nationalpeaceacademy.us).

National War Tax Resistance Coordinating Committee [NWTRCC] (TR RA PA), PO Box 150553, Brooklyn, NY 11215 (+1-718-768 3420) (nwtrcc@nwtrcc.org) (www.nwtrcc.org). *More Than a Paycheck.*

Natural Resources Defense Council [NRDC] (EL), 40 West 20th St, New York, NY 10011 (+1-212-727 2700) (fax 727 1773) (nrdcinfo@nrdc.org) (www.nrdc.org). Works to protect planet's wildlife and wild places.

Nevada Desert Experience [NDE] (RP ND DA RA), 1420 West Bartlett Ave, Las Vegas, NV 89106-2226 (+1-702-646 4814) (info@nevadadesertexperience.org) (www.nevadadesertexperience.org). *Desert Voices.*

New Yorkers Against Gun Violence [NYAGV] (DA), 87 Lafayette St - 3rd Floor, New York, NY 10013 (+1-212-679 2345) (fax 679 2484) (nyagv@nyagv.org) (nyagv.org).

North American Vegetarian Society (EL PO), PO Box 72, Dolgeville, NY 13329 (+1-518-568 7970) (fax 568 7979) (navs@telenet.net). *Vegetarian Voice.*

Nuclear Age Peace Foundation [NAPF] (PA ND IB RE), PMB 121, 1187 Coast Village Rd - Suite 1, Santa Barbara, CA 93108-2794 (+1-805-965 3443) (fax 568 0466) (wagingpeace@napf.org) (www.wagingpeace.org). *The Sunflower.*

Nuclear Information and Resource Service [NIRS] (EL ND), 6930 Carroll Ave - Suite 340, Takoma Park, MD 20912 (+1-301-270 6477) (fax 270 4291) (timj@nirs.org) (www.nirs.org). *WISE/NIRS Nuclear Monitor.* Works with WISE, Amsterdam, to produce information.

Nuclear Resister (ND RA TR PA), PO Box 43383, Tucson, AZ 85733 (+1-520-323 8697) (fax) (nukeresister@igc.org) (www.nukeresister.org). 4 yrly, $25 ($35 abroad) pa.

Nuclear Watch of New Mexico (ND RA), 903 W Alameda - No 325, Santa Fe, NM 87501 (+1-505-989 7342) (fax) (info@nukewatch.org) (www.nukewatch.org). Research, education and action.

Nuclear Watch South (EL ND), PO Box 8574, Atlanta, GA 31106 (+1-404-378 4263) (info@nonukesyall.org) (www.nonukesyall.org). *Nuclear Watch Tower.*

Nukewatch (EL ND RA PA RE), 740A Round Lake Rd, Luck, WI 54853 (+1-715-472 4185) (nukewatch1@lakeland.ws) (www.nukewatchinfo.org). *Nukewatch Quarterly.*

Oak Ridge Environmental Peace Alliance (ND RA), PO Box 5743, Oak Ridge, TN 37831 (+1-865-483 8202) (orep@earthlink.net) (www.orepa.org).

OneVoice Movement - USA (CD CR), PO Box 1577-OCS, New York, NY 10113 (+1-212-897 3985) (info@OneVoiceMovement.org) (www.onevoicemovement.org). See also under Israel, Palestine, and Britain.

Orthodox Peace Fellowship [OPF] (RP), PO Box 6009, Raleigh, NC 27628-2009 (jhforest@gmail.com) (www.incommunion.org). *In Communion.*

Pace e Bene (RP PA), PO Box 2460, Athens, OH 45701-5260 (+1-510-268 8765) (fax 702-648 2281) (info@paceebene.org) (www.paceebene.org). For nonviolence and cultural transformation.

Pathways to Peace (CD RE), PO Box 1057, Larkspur, CA 94977 (+1-415-461 0500) (fax 925 0330) (info@pathwaystopeace.org) (www.pathwaystopeace.org).

Pax Christi USA (PC CD ED), 415 Michigan Ave NE - Suite 240, Washington, DC 20017-4503 (+1-202-635 2741) (info@paxchristiusa.org) (www.paxchristiusa.org).

Peace & Justice Program of the United Methodist Church (RP), c/o General Board of Global Ministries, 475 Riverside Drive, New York, NY 10115 (info@gbgm-umc.org) (new.gbgm-umc.org).

Peace Abbey Foundation (RP PA RE), 16 Lavender St, Millis, MA 02054 (+1-508-655 2143) (administration@peaceabbey.org) (www.peaceabbey.org). Includes Pacifist Living History Museum.

Peace Action (IB ND AT), Montgomery Center, 8630 Fenton St - Suite 524, Silver Spring, MD 20910 (+1-301-565 4050) (fax 565 0850) (kmartin@peace-action.org) (www.peace-action.org).

Peace Alliance (RE PO CR CD), 2108 Military Rd, Arlington, VA 22207 (1-202-684 2553) (info@thepeacealliance.org) (peacealliance.org).

Peace and Justice Studies Association [PJSA] (RE), 1421 37th St NW - Suite 130, Poulton Hall, Georgetown University, Washington, DC 20057 (+1-202-681 2057) (info@peacejusticestudies.org) (www.peacejusticestudies.org).

Peace Brigades International [PBI-USA] (PA RA CR), 1326 9th St NW, Washington, DC 20001 (+1-202-232 0142) (fax 232 0143) (info@pbiusa.org) (www.pbiusa.org).

Peace Development Fund [PDF] (HR EL PA), PO Box 40250, San Francisco, CA 94140 (+1-415-642 0900) (peacedevfund@gmail.com) (www.peacedevelopmentfund.org). *Peace Developments.*

Peaceworkers (CR CD PA RA SD), 721 Shrader St, San Francisco, CA 94117 (+1-415-751 0302) (fax) (davidrhartsough@gmail.com) (www.peaceworkersus.org). Promote international peace teams.

Physicians Committee for Responsible Medicine [PCRM] (PO), 5100 Wisconsin Av NW - Suite 400, Washington, DC 20016 (+1-202-686 2210) (fax 686 2216) (pcrm@pcrm.org) (www.pcrm.org). *Good Medicine.*

Physicians for Social Responsibility [PSR] (IP), 1111 14th St NW - Suite 700, Washington, DC 20005 (+1-202-667 4260) (fax 667 4201) (psrnatl@psr.org) (www.psr.org).

Ploughshares Fund (ND), 1808 Wedemeyer St - Suite 200, The Presidio of San Francisco, San Francisco, CA 94129 (+1-415-668 2244) (fax 668 2214) (ploughshares@ploughshares.org) (www.ploughshares.org). Promoting elimination of nuclear weapons.

Plowshares Network (RP RA ND PA), c/o Jonah House, 1301 Moreland Av, Baltimore, MD 21216 (+1-410-233 6238) (disarmnow@verizon.net) (www.jonahhouse.org)

Positive Futures Network, 284 Madrona Way NE - Suite 116, Bainbridge Island, WA 98110 (+1-206-842 0216) (fax 842 5208) (info@yesmagazine.org) (www.yesmagazine.org). *Yes!.*

Presbyterian Peace Fellowship [PPF] (FR), 17 Cricketown Rd, Stony Point, NY 10980 (+1-845-786 6743) (info@presbypeacefellowship.org) (presbypeacefellowship.org).

Project on Youth and Non-Military Opportunities [Project YANO] (RE PA), PO Box 230157, Encinitas, CA 92023 (+1-760-634 3604) (projyano@aol.com) (www.projectyano.org).

Proposition One Campaign (ND AT), 401 Wilcox Rd, Tryon, NC 28782 (+1-202-210 3886) (et@prop1.org) (prop1.org). For nuclear weapons abolition.

Psychologists for Social Responsibility [PsySR] (ND RE CR), c/o Brad Olsen, 122 S Michigan Ave, National Louis University, Chicago, IL 60603 (+1-917-626 7571) (fax 312-261 3464) (info@psysr.org) (psysr.org).

Random Acts of Kindness Foundation [RAK] (CD CR PO), 1727 Tremont Pl, Denver, CO 80202 (+1-303-297 1964) (fax 297 2919) (info@randomactsofkindness.org) (www.randomactsofkindness.org).

Refuser Solidarity Network (PA HR), PO Box 75392, Washington, DC 20013 (+1-202-232 1100) (info@refusersolidarity.net) (www.refusersolidarity.net). Supports Israeli COs and resisters.

Religions for Peace USA (RE RP CR HR), 777 UN Plaza - 9th Floor, New York, NY 10017 (+1-212-338 9140) (fax 983 0566) (rfpusa@rfpusa.org) (www.rfpusa.org).

Renounce War Projects (RP PA), 8001 Geary Blvd, San Francisco, CA 94121 (+1-415-307 1213) (peacematters@renouncewarprojects.org) (renouncewarprojects.org). Promotes Gandhian ideals.

Reprieve US (HR), PO Box 3627, New York, NY 10163 (+1-917-855 8064) (info@reprieve.org) (www.reprieve.org). Supports people facing death penalty.

Resistance Studies Initiative - Critical Support of People Power and Social Change (RE RA WR), University of Massachusetts Department of Sociology, 200 Hicks Way - Thompson Hall, Amherst, MA 01003-9277 (+1-413-545 5957) (fax 545 3204) (resist@umass.edu) (www.umass.edu/resistancestudies). *Journal of Resistance Studies.*

Resource Center for Nonviolence [RCNV] (WR FR HR), 612 Ocean St, Santa Cruz, CA (+1-831-423 1626) (rcnvinfo@gmail.com) (rcnv.org).

Rising Tide North America [RTA] (EL RA), 268 Bush St - Box 3717, San Francisco, CA 94101 (+1-503-438 4697) (networking@risingtidenorthamerica.org) (risingtidenorthamerica.org). Network of groups working on climate change.

Rocky Mountain Peace and Justice Centre (ND PA RE), PO Box 1156, Boulder, CO 80306 (+1-303-444 6981) (fax 720-565 9755) (www.rmpjc.org).

Ruckus Society (RA), PO Box 28741, Oakland, CA 94604 (+1-510-931 6339) (fax 866-778 6374) (ruckus@ruckus.org) (www.ruckus.org). Tools and training for direct action.

Salam Institute for Peace & Justice (RE RP CR HR), 1628 16th St NW, Washington, DC 20009 (+1-202-360 4955) (info@salaminstitute.org) (salaminstitute.org).

Satyagraha Institute (RP PA PO), c/o Carl Kline, 825 Fourth St, Brookings, SD 57006 (www.satyagrahainstitute.org). Promotes understanding of satyagraha.

School for Conflict Analysis and Resolution [S-CAR] (RE CR TW), George Mason University, 3351 Fairfax Dr - MS 4D3, Arlington, VA 22201 (+1-703-993 1300) (fax 993 1302) (scarmgr@gmu.edu) (scar.gmu.edu).

School of the Americas Watch [SOA Watch] (HR), 5525 Illinois Ave NW, Washington, DC 20011 (+1-202-234 3440) (info@soaw.org) (www.soaw.org).

Seeds of Peace (CD CR PO), 370 Lexington Ave - Suite 1201, New York, NY 10017 (+1-212-573 8040) (fax 573 8047) (info@seedsofpeace.org) (www.seedsofpeace.org). Brings together teenagers from conflict areas.

September 11th Families for Peaceful Tomorrows [PT] (CD CR RE), PO Box 20145, Park West Finance Station, New York, NY 10025 (+1-212-598 0970) (info@peacefultomorrows.org) (peacefultomorrows.org). Promote nonviolent resolution of conflict.

Service Civil International / International Voluntary Service [SCI-IVS USA] (SC), PO Box 1082, Great Barrington, MA 01230 (+1-413-591 8050) (fax 434-366 3545) (sciivs.usa.ltv@gmail.com) (www.volunteersciusa.org).

Sikh Human Rights Group (HR CR), 103 Omar Ave, Evenel, NJ 07001 (shrgusa@shrg.net) (shrg.net).

Swarthmore College Peace Collection (RE), 500 College Ave, Swarthmore, PA 19081 (+1-610-328 8557) (fax 328 8544) (wchmiel1@swarthmore.edu) (www.swarthmore.edu/Library/peace). Also houses Global Nonviolent Action Database.

Syracuse Cultural Workers (HR PA EL PO), PO Box 6367, Syracuse, NY 13217 (+1-315-474 1132) (fax 234 0930) (scw@syracuseculturalworkers.com) (www.syracuseculturalworkers.com). *Peace Calendar*, *Women Artists Datebook*.

Syracuse Peace Council (PA EL RA), 2013 East Genesee St - 2nd Floor, Syracuse, NY 13210 (+1-315-472 5478) (www.peacecouncil.net). *Peace Newsletter*.

The Progressive (HR), 30 W Mifflin St - Suite 703, Madison, WI 53703 (+1-608-257 4626) (editorial@progressive.org) (www.progressive.org). Mthly, $32 ($80 abroad) pa.

Torture Abolition and Survivor Support Coalition [TASSC] (HR AT CR), 4121 Harewood Rd NE - Suite B, Washington, DC 20017 (+1-202-529 2991) (fax 529 8334) (info@tassc.org) (www.tassc.org).

Training for Change (RA RE PO), PO Box 30914, Philadelphia, PA 19104 (+1-267-289 2288) (info@trainingforchange.org) (www.trainingforchange.org).

Tri-Valley CAREs (ND EL), 2582 Old First St, Livermore, CA 94550 (+1-925-443 7148) (fax 443 0177) (marylia@earthlink.net) (www.trivalleycares.org). *Citizen's Watch*. Communities Against a Radioactive Environment.

United for Peace and Justice (DA), PO Box 607, Times Square Station, New York, NY 10108 (+1-212-868 5545) (info@unitedforpeace.org) (www.unitedforpeace.org). Major coalition - especially re Iraq war.

United National Antiwar Coalition [UNAC] (DA), PO Box 123, Delmar, NY 12054 (+1-518-227 6947) (UNACpeace@gmail.com) (www.UNACpeace.org).

United States Institute of Peace [USIP] (RE), 2301 Constitution Ave NW, Washington, DC 20037 (+1-202-457 1700) (fax 429 6063) (www.usip.org). *Peace Watch*.

US Peace Council [USPC] (WP ND AT), 20 Mumford Rd, New Haven, CT 06515 (+1-203-387 0370) (fax 397 2539) (USPC@uspeacecouncil.org) (www.uspeacecouncil.org).

US Peace Memorial Foundation (RE PA), 334 East Lake Rd - No 136, Palm Harbor, FL 34685 (+1-202-455 8776) (info@USPeaceMemorial.org) (www.uspeacememorial.org). Produces US Peace Registry.

US Servas (SE), 1125 16th St - Suite 201, Arcata, CA 95521-5585 (+1-707-825 1714) (admin@usservas.org) (www.usservas.org). *Open Doors*.

Violence Policy Center (RE), 1730 Rhode Island Ave NW - Suite 1014, Washington, DC 20036 (+1-202-822 8200) (www.vpc.org). "Most aggressive group" in US gun control movement.

Voices for Creative Nonviolence (RE), 1249 W Argyle St - No 2, Chicago, IL 60640 (+1-773-878 3815) (info@vcnv.org) (vcnv.org).

Volunteers for Peace [VFP] (WC HR PO CD EL), 7 Kilburn St - Ste 316, Burlington, VT 05410 (+1-802-540 3040) (info@vfp.org) (www.vfp.org).

Waging Nonviolence, PO Box 180369, Brooklyn, New York, NY 11218 (contact@wagingnonviolence.org) (wagingnonviolence.org). Internet-based resource.

War Resisters League [WRL] (WR IB TR AT), 168 Canal St - 6th Floor, New York, NY 10013 (+1-212-228 0450) (fax 228 6193) (wrl@warresisters.org) (www.warresisters.org).

War Resisters League - New England Regional Office (WR), PO Box 1093, Norwich, CT 06360 (+1-860-639 8834) (joanne@warresisters.org) (www.warresisters.org/new-england-office).

Washington Peace Center (HR PA RE), 1525 Newton St NW, Washington, DC 20010 (+1-202-234 2000) (fax 558 5685) (info@washingtonpeacecenter.org) (washingtonpeacecenter.net).

Witness for Peace [WfP] (RP HR TW), 1616 P St NW - Suite 100, Washington, DC 20036 (+1-202-547 6112) (fax 536 4708) (witness@witnessforpeace.org) (www.witnessforpeace.org).

Women Against Military Madness [WAMM] (ND PA RE), 4200 Cedar Ave South - Suite 3, Minneapolis, MN 55407 (+1-612-827 5364) (fax 827 6433) (wamm@mtn.org) (womenagainstmilitarymadness.org).

Women for Genuine Security (CD PA), 965 62nd St, Oakland, CA 94608 (+1-415-312 5583) (info@genuinesecurity.org) (www.genuinesecurity.org).

Women for Women International (HR TW), 2000 M St NW - Suite 200, Washington, DC 20036 (+1-202-737 7705) (fax 737 7709) (general@womenforwomen.org) (www.womenforwomen.org).

Women's Environment and Development Organization [WEDO] (TW EL HR), 355 Lexington Av - 3rd floor, New York, NY 10017 (+1-212-973 0325) (wedo@wedo.org) (www.wedo.org).

Women's International League for Peace and Freedom - US Section [WILPF US] (WL HR), 11 Arlington St - 3rd Floor, Boston, MA 02116 (+1-617-266 0999) (fax 266 1688) (info@wilpf.org) (www.wilpfus.org). *Peace and Freedom.*

Working Group for Peace and Demilitarization in Asia & the Pacific (DA RE), 2161 Massachusetts Ave, Cambridge, MA 02141 (+1-617-661 6130) (info@asiapacificinitiative.org) (www.asiapacificinitiative.org).

World Beyond War (PA DA), PO Box 1484, Charlottesville, VA 22902 (research@worldbeyondwar.org) (worldbeyondwar.org).

World Future Society (PO), 333 N LaSalle St, Chicago, IL 60654 (info@wfs.org) (wfs.site-ym.com). Clearinghouse for ideas about the future.

World Peace Now (CD ND DA), PO Box 275, Point Arena, CA 95468 (ellen.rosser@gmail.com).

World Policy Institute (HR WF), 108 West 39th St - Suite 1000, New York, NY 10018 (+1-212-481 5005) (fax 481 5009) (wpi@worldpolicy.org) (www.worldpolicy.org). *World Policy Journal.*

Worldwatch Institute (EL AT), 1400 16th St NW - Suite 430, Washington, DC 20036 (+1-202-745 8092) (fax 478 2534) (worldwatch@worldwatch.org) (www.worldwatch.org). Europe office in Copenhagen (+45-2087 1933).

URUGUAY

Amnistía Internacional Uruguay (AI), Wilson Ferreira Aldunate 1220, Montevideo 11100 (+598-2-900 7939) (fax 900 9851) (oficina@amnistia.org.uy) (www.amnistia.org.uy).

UZBEKISTAN

"Esperanto" Xalqaro Do'stlik Klubi / International Friendship Club "Esperanto" (CD), c/o PO Box 76, 703000 Samarkand (+998-66-233 1753).

Servas (SE), c/o PO Box 76, 140100 Samarkand (+998-66-233 1753) (imps86@yahoo.com).

Xalqaro Tinchlik va Birdamlik Muzei / Internacia Muzeo de Paco kaj Solidaro (IB RE CD), PO Box 76, 140100 Samarkand (+998-66-233 1753) (fax) (imps86@yahoo.com) (peace.museum.com).

International Museum of Peace and Solidarity.

VENEZUELA

Programa Venezolnao de Educación-Acción en Derechos Humanos [PROVEA] (HR), Apdo Postal 5156, Carmelitas 1010-A, Caracas (+58-212-862 1011) (fax) (www.derechos.org.ve).

VIETNAM

Vietnam Peace Committee [VPC] (WP), 105a Quan Thanh, Ba Dinh, Ha Noi (+84-4-3945 4272) (fax 3733 0201) (vietpeacecom@gmail.com).

ZAMBIA

OneWorld Africa [OWA] (TW), PO Box 37011, Lusaka (+260-21-129 2740) (fax 129 4188) (priscilla.jere@oneworld.net) (africa.oneworld.net). Part of OneWorld Network, in 11 countries.

Zambian Health Workers for Social Responsibility [ZHSR] (HR), c/o Department of Medicine, School of Medicine, PO Box 50110, Lusaka (bobmtonga@hotmail.com).

ZIMBABWE

Gays and Lesbians of Zimbabwe [GALZ] (WR HR), Private Bag A6131, Avondale, Harare (+263-4-741736) (fax 740614) (info@galz.co.zw) (www.galz.co.zw). *Galzette.*

Practical Action Southern Africa (EL TW PO), 4 Ludlow Road, off Enterprise Road, Newlands, Harare (+263-4-776631) (fax 788157) (info@practicalaction.org.zw) (practicalaction.org/southern-africa). Formerly Intermediate Technology Development Group.

Society of Friends (SF), 3 Vincent Ave, Belvedere, Harare (+263-4-778028) (rknottenbelt621@gmail.com).

South-North Centre for Peacebuilding and Development [SNCPD] (RE TW), PO Box HG358, Highlands, Harare (+263-4-339337) (fax).

Students for Environmental Action [SEA] (EL), c/o Institute of Environmental Studies, University of Zimbabwe, PO Box MP, 167 Mount Pleasant, Harare (+263-4-301925) (fax 332853) (seazim@ivillage.com) (www.uz.ac.zw/sea).

Women of Zimbabwe Arise [WOZA] (HR), PO Box FM701, Famona, Bulawayo (info@wozazimbabwe.org) (wozazimbabwe.org).

Zimbabwe Human Rights NGO Forum (HR), PO Box 9077, 8th Floor, Bluebridge, Eastgate, Harare (+263-4-250511) (fax 250494) (admin@hrforum.co.zw) (www.hrforumzim.com).

Zimbabwe Lawyers for Human Rights [ZLHR] (HR), Box CY 1393, Causeway, Harare (+263-4-764085) (fax 705641) (info@zlhr.org.zw) (www.zlhr.org.zw).

Notes

Notes